G000270850

The Walmsley Society
www.walmsleysoc.org

Leo Walmsley

THE
HAPPY
ENDING

by

Leo Walmsley

The Walmsley Society

First published in 1957 by Collins
This edition published in 2013 by
The Walmsley Society
www.walmsleysoc.org

ISBN   978-0-9561151-6-4

British Library Cataloguing-in-Publication Data:
A catalogue record is available for this book
from the British Library.

Cover design by Margaret and Graham Higson

Font used on the cover for
The Happy Ending
© 2008 Essqué Productions

Printed and bound by
SRP
Exeter

To
AMY, SARA, RITA
AND JACK

my dear friends of the
Pen Pom Pren, Drefach,
for all their kindness
to me.

1

IT WAS a cold, windy, rainy November night in the second autumn of the war when our train arrived at the little country station in Pembrokeshire with a polysyllabic, and to us, unpronounceable name, which, we had been told in a letter by the man who had sold it to us, was the nearest passenger railway station to our new home.

The train was a stopping train from Cardiff to the west coast, and it was more than an hour late. There had been an air-raid warning at Swansea (which had already suffered severe bombing). We'd had to keep the blinds of the compartment tightly drawn. All the stations we had halted at were dimly lit, and their names removed in order to confuse any possible Nazi parachutist, spy or invader, although by this time the chance of an invasion of Great Britain seemed very remote.

I got out first to make certain that we were at the right place. The guard, himself a very harassed man, reassured me.

"Yes, yes. This is it. Come on now, hurry. Let's have your luggage from the van."

Although the train was crowded, chiefly with service men and women bound for the military and naval bases of Pembroke Dock and Milford Haven, there were no other passengers getting out or getting in. The station was deserted, apart from one elderly porter, who, urgently summoned by the guard, was trundling an inadequate hand-barrow towards the van, and a stoutish, red-faced, jovial-looking man in a thick overcoat, a bowler hat, with a muffler round his neck, standing near the WAY OUT, looking as though he had come to meet someone.

I rushed back to the compartment.

"Come on," I said to Dain. "This is it. Come on kids!"

My wife and the children (all except Timothy, our last-born, who was fast asleep) got out. I picked up Timothy, then, handing him to Dain to hold, hurried back to the van to see that all our luggage had been safely offloaded. I apologised to the guard for the number and weight of them.

At last they were all out. I tipped him far more than I could afford. He seemed surprised and a little less bothered, said it had been no trouble at all, and blew his whistle. The train moved out, and as it did so the platform was exposed to the full strength of the driving rain and the wind, which was blowing a full gale from the southwest.

Dain had moved with the children into the relative shelter of the station building. It was the porter—it soon transpired that he combined the duties of stationmaster, signalman and ticket collector—who was now harassed. He had no overcoat. His hat blew off in a sudden fierce gust of wind, and in trying to retrieve it the hand-barrow toppled over, its load slithering on to the wet asphalt.

Then, laughing, and shouting something in Welsh, the stoutish man came to our help. The hat was rescued. Our luggage was carried in out of the rain. I thanked the man for his kindness. He grinned benignly.

The porter, wiping the rain from his face, and assuming his second role, asked for our tickets. They were paper ones, not cardboard, their destination written in by hand by the ticket clerk of our own Yorkshire railway station, who had joked about the spelling of the name. The porter, now quite recovered, laughed too.

"The clerk who made these out for you was a poor speller or he couldn't have known Wales. He's got all his *ys* and *lls* mixed up. It's a long way you've come."

"Yes," I said, "and we've still got a long way to go. Is there a garage near here where we can hire a car?"

"No. There's no garage here nearer than six miles, and no one's got petrol these days. Where would you be wanting to go?"

"The place is called Castle Druid. It's about twelve miles away."

"Castle Druid? Never heard of it."

The stoutish man, who all the time had been regarding us with growing amusement and curiosity, joined in.

"What, never heard of Castle Druid? And you a Welshman? Don't show your ignorance. Why it's a famous place. One of the most beautiful places in Pembrokeshire. It's in a little valley called Cwm Gloyne, running down from Mynydd Parfor, which means the Purple Mountain. It's not a castle, but it's supposed there was a druid temple near, and it's not far from there the druids got the stones to build Stonehenge. Fancy a Welshman like yourself not having heard of Castle Druid!"

"I'm a Cardiff man now, born and bred, and wouldn't be here in this godforsaken place but for the war."

"Well, it's famous. There's a story that Lord Nelson stayed there with Lady Hamilton, when he was stationed at Milford Haven. It must have been a grand place then, with an ornamental lake and lawns and gardens. A pity it was all allowed to go to rack and ruin. But what are you going there for, if you don't mind my asking?"

I liked the man and did not in any way resent his curiosity.

"We're going to live there," I said.

He looked astonished.

"*Live* there? Do you know it? Have you seen it?"

"No. We've taken it on spec. Our small farm in Yorkshire has been requisitioned for opencast mining, and the whole district scheduled as a battle-training ground. We've bought Castle Druid. The man we bought it from made it clear that the whole place was in a pretty bad state, both buildings and land, but we're hoping to find that part of the house is habitable."

"But man, it's terrible! The last time I saw it there was a great hole in the roof, you could see the rafters showing, and one of the main walls had a bulge, and I'd not be surprised if that wall was flat now. You couldn't live with small children in a place like that!"

Our eldest daughter, Amelia, aged ten, who could appear disconcertingly grown up at times, remarked airily:

4

"Oh that wouldn't frighten us. We're quite used to it. The first place we lived in, where I was born, was just a wooden hut, and it leaked like mad until Daddy mended the roof. And the next place hadn't a roof at all at first."

"Don't exaggerate, Amelia," Dain laughed. "We didn't live in it like that. That was the barn before it was pulled down to build our house."

Both men were laughing. And the porter-cum-ticket-clerk now assumed his third and fourth roles.

"Come on now into the office, where there's a nice fire. It's cold out here."

It was the combined station-master's ticket, parcel and signal room, and there was a blazing coal fire. He pushed a chair up to the fire and invited my wife to sit down. The jovial man (I observed now that he smelled rather strongly of alcohol) followed us in.

"I'm very troubled about your going out there to Castle Druid on a dark stormy night like this, in spite of what your little girl says. She's a caution isn't she? Is it a farmer you are? You don't look like one if I may say so."

"No. I'm an author. I was in the RAF in the last war. Invalided out. They wouldn't take me back for this one, and as we had about forty acres of rough land, we started ploughing some of it up, thinking we'd run the place as a farm and produce food. Then we found there was a thick bed of ganister under the subsoil. The stuff needed for lining of furnaces. More important to the war effort than oats."

Our second daughter Jane, who, like Amelia, had no inhibitions, joined in the discussion.

"We've got a pony. Her name is Annabella. She's such

5

a darling. She's coming in a motor van. We've got lots of hens and ducks. We're going to get more ponies too, and cows. We've got a trap for Annabella that Daddy made from an old motor car."

"Don't be silly, Jane," her sister rebuked, "it was only the wheels that came from a motor car. The shafts came from an old trap that somebody gave us."

Both men seemed highly amused by this, and the stoutish one guffawed, but he quickly returned to his cross-examination.

"Did you say you were an author? Might I ask your name?"

I told him, and I guessed by his expression what he was going to say next.

"Do you write under your own name?"

"Yes."

He looked apologetic.

"I don't think I can have come across any of your books. But I'm not much of a book reader. Now if you'd been any sort of a musician with a name, I'd have heard of you. We're all great lovers of music in Wales, especially singing. Have you ever heard a good Welsh choir singing *Land of Our Fathers* or a chorus from the *Messiah*? Oh, it's a wonderful thing. But never mind that now. I'm very troubled about your going off to Castle Druid. I take it this charming-looking young lady is your wife. My name is a very unusual one for a Welshman. It's Jones. Eddy Jones. I'm a builders' and agricultural merchant. Every farmer for miles around knows me."

We shook hands, and I formally introduced him to my wife, to Amelia and Jane and Angus, who was rapturously studying the signal levers. Timothy had passed out again on Dain's lap.

"You've got a fine healthy brood of children, and no mistake," he went on, "I'm a family man myself, but all my children are grown up and away, and I've been thinking my wife would have liked you all to have stayed with us this night, but she's away in Aberystwyth visiting one of our married daughters, and I haven't washed up the dishes since she went. But I've got an idea. There's no car you can hire that will take you to Castle Druid this night, and *I* won't take you there. I wouldn't have such a thing on my conscience."

"We were," I said, "hoping we could find some inn or farm nearby where we could spend at least one night. I don't know if our furniture has arrived there yet."

"You've read my mind! The nearest village to Castle Druid has an English name, Castlebridge, and there's a pub there called the Jew's Harp. It's not a very fancy sort of place. It's only a country pub, but the folks who own it have hearts of gold, and they are all dear friends of mine. Their name is Evans, another unusual Welsh name, eh? They're farmers too in a small way with about eighty acres of land. There's Mother Evans—eighty-four, and still as frisky as a lamb, and Tom Evans, the son, and two sisters, Amy and Sara, a widow. Tom's a great singer, with a sweet tenor voice, and he'd have won prizes at the National Eisteddfod if he'd had the courage to compete. There's a niece too who lives close to. them, Mano Evans. A pretty girl, a school teacher and she plays the piano like a professional. But they're all singers or musicians at the Jew's Harp, and Tom's a special pal of mine. And I'll let you into a secret now. It's my birthday today. I'm here to the station to meet another pal of mine from Swansea. We were going to have a drive round and meet a few friends, and maybe have a drink or two, but it's clear he hasn't turned up, and there's nothing I'd like better than to go out and see Tom Evans and have a bit of a sing-song. There's plenty of accommodation in the old pub. They'll make you feel at home, especially when they see your children."

I felt rather overwhelmed.

"It is good of you. But we're such a crowd. And there's an awful lot of luggage."

"Don't worry about that. I've got a shooting-brake, and being on agricultural business, I get all the petrol I want. Now come on. Dai here won't mind going out in the wet again to get your things on board. You stay here by the fire, lady, with the baby, till we're all packed up."

Neither of us had been in Wales before. We had been warned that we would find the Welsh people, especially those of the rural areas, suspicious of strangers, unfriendly, very difficult to get on with. The few Welshmen I had met in my life, however, I had liked. Although a Yorkshireman, I had enough Irish blood in me to be in tune with the Celtic temperament. I had a great admiration for certain Welsh writers, artists, actors and musicians. I *had* heard (over the radio) a Welsh choir singing *Land of Our Fathers*. And I cherished, like most men who had served in the Kaiser's war, a very special affection for our wartime Prime Minister, David Lloyd George. Here I thought was a most propitious start to a venture which grim circumstance had forced upon us. If the rest of the people we were going to live among were like Eddy Jones, things were not going to be so bad. And his gloomy remarks about our new home did not seriously disturb me. We knew that things were going to be difficult and tough.

The car, a most impressive vehicle with its long varnished timber body, was drawn up in the lee of the station buildings. The children argued as to who should sit next to Eddy in the front seat. When all our luggage was on board, the matter was settled by Amelia joining us in the rear seats, with the cynical observation that there was no point in being in the front, as it was too dark to see anything. I thanked and tipped the genial railway official, and Eddy, suddenly bursting into song, and of all songs *O Sole Mio*, started the engine, and away we went.

I had now got Timothy, still asleep, in my arms. Our seats were well back, and there was no fear of our being overheard.

"What a bit of luck," I said to Dain.

"He's wonderful, isn't he? But I think he's a bit tight! I hope we're going to be all right," she added, a little apprehensively.

"He does sound happy, but I think he's a good driver."

My remark sprang from a fatalistic optimism that I'd always found it best to assume when travelling in motor cars or aeroplanes or any other form of rapid transport. One just had to hope for the best. It was a powerful car. Soon we were travelling at great speed. We could see nothing through the windows, because of the rain, and ahead the single regulation hooded driving light just made a dim orange halo. But judging by the way we lurched and dipped and climbed (occasionally in low gear) we were travelling along a twisting hilly lane, a by-lane, for there was no other traffic. And all the time Eddy sang, bits out of grand opera, Gilbert and Sullivan, Handel, Bach and even Moody and Sankey. He had a most agreeable baritone voice.

Then we slowed down, and he drew in alongside a whitewashed building, close up to the roadside and stopped.

"We're not there yet," he said. "I've got a call to make, and I won't be more than a minute or two."

He got out, slamming the door behind him, and disappeared. There was an uncanny silence in the car, which was in complete darkness. I rubbed the steam from the side window and peered out, but I could only see the vague outline of the building, which was showing no lights.

"I think it must be a pub," I said, rather apprehensively, to Dain. She did not reply, and I suddenly realised that both she and Amelia had fallen asleep. It was not surprising. We had been travelling since yesterday afternoon. The children had managed to get some sleep in the train, and various waiting-rooms of our many changing stations, but we'd had none. It was very warm in the car. I couldn't keep my own eyes open, and I would have fallen asleep if I hadn't been roused by Eddy's return. He opened the door.

"Come on, Jane, move up and let me get in! Why they're both fast asleep, arm in arm, like the babes in the wood."

He switched on a ceiling light. Angus and Jane had woken up and were rubbing their eyes. Eddy had shut the door. I saw that he had a bottle in his hand and another in his pocket. He carefully stowed them under his seat.

"We shan't be long now," he said, "this is The Marquis of Milford. It's a favourite spot for anglers in the spring and summer but very quiet in winter. I had to get a bottle here to make sure, for there's a shortage of Scotch at the present time, and it's as likely as not they'll be out of it at the Jew's Harp. It's the only stuff I drink when I'm having a night out, and it doesn't do to mix your drinks. Would you like a nip before we start?"

I declined with thanks, but by the smell I guessed that he had taken the opportunity for a quick one while he had been buying his bottles. Yet he wasn't drunk, and certainly he was not incapable. He switched off the light, pressed the starting knob, and as we moved off, he started to sing again.

It was still raining and blowing hard. The road continued to twist and rise and fall, like a scenic railway. And then after one long climb, we began to descend a very steep hill, so steep that he kept the car in low gear, and for the first time he stopped singing.

"It's a nasty bit this. I once saw a milk lorry loaded with empty churns come down here when there was ice on the road! The tyres wouldn't hold and she took charge, but the driver had the sense to turn into the hedge. She capsized, and man, you never heard such a noise as those churns running down the hill. . .

"Well, here's Castlebridge at the hill bottom. It's only

11

a small village, maybe fifty houses, but it's one of the prettiest spots in Wales. The Jew's Harp's dead in the middle of it, close by the bridge."

We were on the level for a hundred yards or so. Then, pulling in to the near side of the road, he slowed and stopped.

"Here we are. I'm thinking I'd best go in first, and have a word with them. It will be all right I'm sure. I won't be a minute."

He switched on the light again, and got out. I lowered the nearside window. I could vaguely distinguish a long, low, white-washed building with small chinks of light showing round the edges of their blackout blinds. Immediately opposite was a roofed porch with an outer and an inner door. As Eddy opened the inner one there was a blaze of light, the sound of many voices, male and female, laughing, jabbering in Welsh. They were silenced dramatically. Then there was a tumult of shouts in which I heard words.

"Eddy *bach*. Eddy *bach*!"

I saw a dark-haired middle-aged woman rush forward and embrace him.

The door was shut again.

I roused my sleeping or semi-sleeping family. Before Dain had time to regain full consciousness, the door opened, and Eddy appeared again with the same woman and another. They all came forward, and Eddy opened the door.

"Come on now, get out. Everything's O.K. Everything's beautiful!"

Indifferent to the pelting rain, the two women helped

the children out, and one of them took Angus in her arms and hurried him inside the porch. I handed Timothy out to the other one, and she cried:

"Oh, what a darling boy. Look at him. Fast asleep. Poor little boy."

A man had appeared too.

"You get the luggage out, Tom *bach*," Eddy shouted, "and you people hurry inside out of the rain."

We might have been a family of wealthy American tourists arriving at a Continental hotel, the fuss that was being made of us, yet there was nothing obsequious about it. Two more men came out, and one of them took the suitcase I was carrying, in spite of my protests.

"Get inside, get inside," they were shouting.

There was a passage leading from the porch, and low-ceilinged rooms on either side. The one on the left was crowded with men, fuggy with tobacco smoke, lit by a large hanging oil lamp. It was the bar-room, although there was no bar, only tables and benches. There was a cavernous open fireplace with a log fire, with high-backed wooden settles. The other room was the parlour. There was a sofa in it, upholstered chairs, a big round dining table, a what-not table with a flowering geranium on it, growing from a shining copper bowl. There was a Victorian fireplace with tiled surrounds, and drawn up to this was another high-backed settle, on which was seated a handsome white-haired lady dressed in black, but with a red shawl over her shoulders. There was knitting on her lap. And, on its haunches, close up to her on the settle was a magnificent collie with the most human and intelligent and benevolent face.

13

We were all ushered into this room. To my embarrassment, Eddy introduced us to the old lady as the squire of Castle Druid, his wife and family. The lady herself was Mother Evans. She was not as Eddy had said, as frisky as a lamb, but her eyes were bright, her mind alert, and it was clear at once, that although kind, she was the autocratic boss of the establishment.

Dain and I shook hands with her. I introduced all the children to her, one by one. Eddy gave her an account of how he had met us at the railway station, of what I had told him of our affairs. The old lady listened intently, punctuating his narrative now and again with "*ody ody*," which I took to mean "yes yes"; and the dog kept on looking from Eddy to us and the old lady as though it understood every word that was said.

"Well, well. You were quite right, Eddy *bach*, not to let them go to Castle Druid this night. I haven't seen the mansion for a long time, but I'm told it's all in ruins. Apart from poor Christmas Morgan there's no one lived in it since the squire with the mad wife was there, and that's forty years ago. A mad creature she was when the moon was full. She'd run out of the house in her nightgown and climb up a tall tree, and when she got to the top scream that she couldn't get down, and they'd have to get a ladder to her. Or she'd jump into the lake. He had the lower branches of all the trees near the house lopped off, and then he had the lake drained. But it was the squire himself who was taken to the asylum in the end, and no wonder, poor man. And it was soon after that she disappeared and so did the young gardener they had, and no one knew what happened to them. Now,

Sara, don't stand there doing nothing. They'll be wanting something to eat and drink. Get them some ham and eggs and tea."

She had addressed the elder of the two women, and to the other, the one who had embraced Eddy so warmly, she said,

"Now Amy. Take the lady upstairs and show her the bedrooms. There's the cot will be all right for the little boy, bless him, and I'd have him there straightaway. Are you going home now, Eddy *bach*?"

Eddy grinned.

"No, Mother. I'm a lonely man with my wife away at Aberystwyth, and it's my birthday too. I'd a mind to stay and have a bit of singing with you all. I've brought some Scotch with me. Would you like a drop now to drink my health?"

"I would indeed. But don't you be getting drunk tonight and disgracing us in front of the English. If your wife's away you'll not have had a proper meal, so you'd better have one now before you start drinking. It will be nice to have a bit of singing. Let the children stay here with me while you're upstairs, for I like the company of them. Come now and sit down near to me and Nellie. She'll not bite."

Dain went off with Amy, who had Timothy in her arms. Eddy signed to me to follow him into the bar-room. I had already identified Tom Evans. He was middle-aged, dark like his sisters, with twinkling eyes, longish black hair and a humorous mouth. There were about a score of other men in the room. All were middle-aged or very old. They were mostly roughly dressed, farmers or farm labourers. One of them, with a straggling grey beard and watery eyes, looked like a tramp. One of them, who looked far too old for the job, was wearing a postman's jacket, which was unbuttoned, showing a rather grimy collarless shirt. He was the first of the company to be introduced by Eddy, in his role of Master of Ceremonies. He was Albert the Post, actually retired but doing the job because the regular postman had been called up.

"You'll have to excuse some of our friends here for not saying much as they don't talk English," he said. "Maybe, however, you'll be speaking the Welsh yourself soon, now you've come to live here, for it's a beautiful language. By the way, they're nearly all Evans or Bowen or Davies in Castlebridge, and that's why they are called after their job, or the farm they own. That's Tom the Smith, next to Albert, and Eddy Hendre by the fire, for Hendre's the name of his farm, and they're all Evans. You'll not find a Jones in Castlebridge."

I was feeling rather dazed. Each man I was introduced to looked a character. It was like a scene in a play or film. I shook hands with them all, then Eddy said:

"Now then. Drinks for everyone, for it's my birthday, but before you drink to that we'll drink the health of the squire. Have what you like, but I have whisky here for those who prefer that to Tom's beer."

Strangely enough I no longer felt embarrassed by my accession to squiredom. I knew that Eddy was indulging in a good-natured leg-pull. He insisted that I should have some of his whisky. Then, after the two toasts had been drunk, he said quite seriously:

"Well, gentlemen, what do you think about our friend here going to Castle Druid to live? You all know it better than I do."

He repeated what was obviously the same question in Welsh.

There was a momentary hush. Then one of the men said:

"He's a brave man, and he must have a brave wife."

"The old mansion is not fit for cattle to live in at present," said another, and there followed a fusillade.

"*Ody ody*. There's a big hole in the roof, and most of the windows are out and there's a tree sprouting out of the wall."

"*Ody ody*, a place for ghosts it is. There's a story that someone was murdered there years ago, and buried in the cellars. And what about Christmas Morgan?"

"Nobody knows yet what happened to the squire's wife and the young man who was supposed to have been her sweetheart. The cellars are all walled up and no one knows exactly where they are."

"There's a tale there was treasure buried somewhere, though no one has found any sign of it yet."

"*Ody ody*. When I was a boy I looked for that treasure, but all I ever found was an old ha'penny of King George the Fourth."

"There's a tree branch has fallen on the stable roof in the great gale last winter."

Some of the men were joining in in Welsh, but suddenly one man whom Eddy had introduced as Clow the Mason, conspicuous as easily the tallest man in the room, banged his fist on the table and shouted:

"*Jowl!* I've never heard such a lot of damn rubbish spoken, with your murders and ghosts and treasure. I know more about Castle Druid than any of you, for I live only a mile from it. By rights I should be the owner of it now. My grandfather Llewellyn Evans was the first son of Squire Vaughan of Castle Druid, who owned most of the land round here in his day. Llewellyn's mother was a maid at the mansion, and the squire had her with child when she was seventeen. By rights he should have married her, and given Llewellyn his name. Why not? She was as good as him. But he married a woman from London city and had a son by her who inherited all his riches when he died. The son was a great drinker and gambler and had sold up most of the estate before he died. *His* son who had the mad wife went mad himself, yet before he was put away the mansion was still a splendid place. My father looked after it and the gardens for the squire's trustees, and I was caretaker myself until Christmas Morgan rented it and let it go to ruin. A beautiful place it was, and could be again with a bit of money spent on it. Any place would look ruined if it was left neglected for years. There *is* a hole in the roof, by damn, and the rain has got in, and there's a floor rotted away. And there's a ceiling down, and some windows out. But it's not all in ruins. A man with money could soon have it right again, for there's a plenty of slates in the quarry, and timber in the wood."

"Well, well," said Eddy. "And what's the land like, Clow, for the squire here plans to farm it. Isn't it all overgrown with furze and fern and weed?"

I imagined that Clow's lips curled slightly at Eddy's

obviously ironic use of the word "squire". But he answered:

"I'm a mason, by damn, not a farmer, like some of you here. I only keep a cow and a few pigs, and grow a few spuds. I only wish I had some of Castle Druid fields. There's the seven-acre pasture round the mansion could grow enough hay to feed three cows through the winter. There's plenty of good grazing in the other fields even if the fern is thick in some of them. If Christmas Morgan had kept off the bottle he could have made the farm pay."

I might have been worried by what some of the others had said, but it was not new to me, except for the reputed ghost and treasure, and the reference to the last tenant of the place, with his peculiar Christian name. We had paid only £750 for Castle Druid (which had been designed by John Nash), with three cottages, farm buildings, woods and fifty acres of land. I had no doubt as to the integrity of the vendor. He had been unable to send a photograph, but he had described its dilapidations in detail, and had even mentioned the stable roof. He had bought it himself with the idea of reclaiming it. The war had interfered with his plans.

I was indeed feeling rather elated, for the whisky was taking effect, and there was something both intriguing and inspiring in what Clow had said. As well as being tall, he was broad, almost gigantic. He looked about sixty, with a deeply-lined face, a long thin nose, a straggling grey moustache with traces of ginger in it, and big tobacco-stained teeth. It was his eyes that impressed me most, however. They were greenish-grey with beetling eyebrows. They were fierce, eagle eyes, reminding me strongly of those of the autocratic squire of my own Yorkshire country district, whom I had dreaded as a boy. In spite of his unkempt appearance and rough working clothes, I could well believe that Clow had in him the blood of a "gentleman".

I said to him:

"I'm not a squire! Eddy's pulling my leg about that. And I haven't much money, but we've got to live in Castle Druid and we've got to make it liveable in. I'll need a mason I expect, and a carpenter too, although I want to do as much as I can myself. Perhaps you'd consider taking on the job?"

Clow gave me a shrewd look, and Tom Evans, who'd been busy with the drinks, yet apparently had missed nothing of the conversation, joined in.

"You'd not find a better man in Wales for doing a job of building than Clow. But he's a terrible man for swearing. You'll have to be careful your children don't learn their Welsh from him. Wouldn't it be a good thing now if I took you out to Castle Druid in the morning in my old car, and Clow would go round the place with you?"

Again Clow gave me a shrewd look.

"I'll do that," he said. "We can talk then. *Jowl*, there's nothing I'd like better than to see the old place beautiful again."

"Come on," I said recklessly, "drinks all around on me."

The conversation became general again, and largely it was in Welsh. I rarely touched alcohol. After my second drink I was not far from being tipsy. Then Sara shouted through the bar-room doorway.

"Come on now, supper's on the table and it will be getting cold."

There was ham and eggs, tea, bread and butter with real butter, Welsh cakes, the first real meal we'd had since leaving home. There was one other guest in addition to Eddy: a short, slim, dark-haired girl of about twenty, with a lovely complexion, beautiful grey eyes and perfect teeth. It was Mano, Tom's schoolteacher niece. The children, although pop-eyed from want of sleep, ate ravenously, but they made no protest when, with supper over, they were hurried off to bed. And, as soon as they were gone, Mano went to the piano. Several of the men from the bar-room came in, and the sing-song began.

There was no more drinking after closing time, when most of the men, including Clow, went home, and the food and the strong tea neutralised what I had taken. Yet I remained agreeably intoxicated. Eddy had been right about the Jew's Harp. They were all, even Mother, musicians, and if Tom modestly declined to give us a solo, both he and Eddy sang straight songs in Welsh, and all joined in the part songs and choruses. Tom's voice, if it lacked power, had a perfect quality.

It was long after midnight when the party broke up. Eddy, definitely tight, yet still fortunately capable, refused the pressing invitations to stay the night. He had his business to attend to in the morning. We thanked him for his almost unbelievable kindness. He wished us good luck with our venture, said he would come out to see us the first chance.

When at last we got to bed, Dain said:

"They're wonderful, wonderful. I've never met people I liked so much. Isn't Mother a marvel? Eighty-four and as gay as any of them. Oh, I'm glad we've come to live in Wales! I'm dying to see the house. I'm sure it's not going to be so bad, that we're going to love it."

I told her about Clow.

"What a romantic story," she said. "I hope he turns up tomorrow."

"Yes. He seems just the very man we want, if the house *is* in such a mess. Well, we'll know about that tomorrow.

2

THE STORM had blown itself out during the night. When I got downstairs next morning (Dain was dressing a very excited Timothy), Amelia, Jane and Angus had already got up. The sun was shining through the open street door. It was a fine autumnal day.

Sara told me that the children had gone with Amy to see the calves, and gather the eggs. Tom had gone off in the car and trailer with the milk, but he would be back any minute. Mother hadn't got up yet. She didn't as a rule do so till dinnertime. There was a fire in the parlour, and breakfast was almost ready.

Sara was several years older than her sister, and less ebullient. Her black hair was shot with silver. She had her mother's good looks, the same high cheekbones and full mouth, but there was the shadow of tragedy in her eyes. Her face was lined and pallid. Clearly she was the housekeeper and cook, and, despite her seniority in years, under Amy's benign domination. She was hurrying now between parlour and kitchen, from which came the pleasant odour of frying ham. I stepped out through the doorway for my first view of Castlebridge.

Eddy had not exaggerated. It *was* a pretty place. To the left, both sides of the level but slightly curving road were lined with squat, slate-roofed cottages, mostly detached, with front gardens. Their walls were lime-washed, but only one or two of them were dead white. Some were salmon pink, some pale blue, some chrome and terracotta.

To the right, there were only farm buildings and a Dutch barn on the opposite side of the road, which shortly rose to the hump of a stone bridge with parapets, and then to the steep wooded hill down which Eddy had driven with special caution. From the doorway I could not see the stream or river the bridge crossed, but the village lay in a level valley, narrowing to the north where there were treeless, rounded hills which reminded me strongly of the moors near our Yorkshire home. It looked as though there might be heather on them.

Suddenly from behind the farm buildings Amy appeared, with Jane holding one of her hands, Angus the other. Amelia was carrying a basket of eggs. They crossed the road, and at the same time a dilapidated

Morris, with trailer behind, came over the bridge and drew up at the doorway. It was Tom, Tom the Harp, I must remember.

He grinned genially.

"Good morning, Squire *bach*. I hope you had a good night's sleep."

He spoke to the children, who now deserted Amy to crowd round his car.

"What do you think of the old bus? A bit of a comedown after Eddy Jones's car, eh? But I only gave thirty pounds for it just before the war. Are you ready now to go to Castle Druid? I'll have the trailer off in a minute."

"Go on now!" cried Amy. "They haven't had breakfast yet."

"We've seen two lovely calves," cried Jane, coming up to me. "Lovely. Shall we have some calves too?"

"We've seen an *engine!*" shouted Angus. "I want to see it go."

"That's my oil engine," laughed Tom, "for working the turnip chopper. I'll show you how it goes one day."

Sara came to the door and called that breakfast was ready.

Amy, it seemed, was the business manager of the Jew's Harp, although all important matters were subject to Mother's sanction. I had a business talk with her after breakfast. We might, I said, have to stay a week at the inn, perhaps longer. I must know her terms.

She was quite embarrassed, and finally gave a figure that was fantastically cheap, and when I told her so she argued that she couldn't charge ordinary hotel prices, that most of the food came from the farm, and it was such a pleasure having us to stay. We finally agreed on a figure that was still, I felt, too low, and she refused to make any charge for Timothy, only she'd like him to stay this morning instead of going with us in the car. She and Sara would look after him all right. Dain agreed. It would make us more mobile for our reconnaissance and Timothy himself did not seem to mind a bit. He had struck up an immediate friendship with Nellie the collie.

"Well, this is it," I said to Dain as we started off. "We'll soon know the worst!"

"And the best," she laughed. "I wonder what the kitchen's going to be like. It can't be worse than our Cornish hut was at first. I'm sure everything's going to be better than we've imagined. I just can't get over the kindness of the people at the Jew's Harp. I love them all. And isn't it lovely country!"

We had crossed the bridge, and I'd had a glimpse of a moderate-sized, swift and clear running stream. But instead of going up the milk-churn hill we turned north up the valley towards the bare hills. Jane and Angus were in the front seat with Tom, and they were chattering away to him. Amelia was with us in the rear. She remarked with childish candour, but fortunately not loud enough for Tom to hear:

"This isn't such a nice car as the one we were in last night. I wish we could have a car like that."

The country was lovely. The valley was sparsely wooded with tall oaks and ash, and the stream meandered through it so that here and there one caught the gleam of water. We were drawing nearer to the bare-topped hill, then shortly the road turned right, away from it, and began to rise, but not steeply. There were high double stone and earth banks on either side of the road, like those in many rural parts of Devon and Cornwall, so high indeed that we might have been passing through a railway cutting. Then the road levelled and began a gradual descent. We saw the hill again and it became clear that we had climbed over a ridge leading from it which formed a watershed of the Castlebridge stream. There was another valley with the glint of another stream in it.

"This is Cwm Gloyne," Tom shouted, pointing to the valley. " 'Cwm' means valley. We'll see Castle Druid in a minute or two."

The road banks were still high, hiding the valley, and the road, although now dead level, twisted. Then, coming round a bend, we saw ahead of us on the left side the end wall of a building, partly obscured by a tall horse-chestnut tree.

"Is that it?" I shouted to Tom.

"Yes, indeed. That's Castle Druid."

I had a sudden horrible sensation in the pit of my stomach. As we drew alongside the building I saw that it consisted of nothing else but three small and very dilapidated cottages, all attached, the far one with a great hole in its roof.

Dain was silent. Amelia said:

"What an awful-looking place. It doesn't look much like a castle. It looks like a slum!"

"Good heavens!" I cried. "Is this Castle Druid?"

Tom laughed.

"Yes indeed. But this isn't the mansion. This is only the cottages. The mansion's down below, out of sight from the road."

We got out, and as we did so a man appeared from the door-less doorway of the nearest cottage. It was Clow the Mason. He looked even bigger than he had done last night in the bar-room. He was well over six feet in height and he held himself erect with his chest thrown out, like a soldier on parade. He was carrying a stout home-made walking-stick. He touched his hat to Dain, and said good morning to me. I felt that I liked him, but he frightened me a little. He lacked the warmth and geniality of the other people we had met. His eyes were fierce, and there was still that shrewd expression in them, as though as yet he hadn't weighed us up. He was a man, I was sure, who was used to having his own way, who would be difficult to cross.

"I'll not come down with you now," said Tom, "for I've got a lot to do. I'll be back here at four o'clock. Clow will take you round the place."

I protested that we could walk back, but Tom laughed.

"Four o'clock!" he repeated, as he started to turn the car round.

Just short of the nearest end wall of the cottages was an ordinary field gate, and this Clow opened.

"This is the nearest way down to the mansion," he said. "The main gate, and it needs a carpenter at it, is away down the road. There used to be a carriage drive from the gate to the front door of the mansion, but it's grown over with the grass. Here's the cowhouse on our right, and the stackyard, and beyond that the stable which the tree branch fell on to. All the farm buildings are here on the same level as the road and the cottages, but the mansion is down below."

It became clear that the cottages and farm buildings were all joined together to enclose three sides of the rectangular stackyard, entry to which was given by tall arched doorways. The ground inside the gate sloped steeply into a grass field for about 30 feet. The walls of the cowhouse (which seemed to be in good repair) were built up against this slope. It was not until we reached the bottom corner of this building that we saw still below us on our right-hand side, the mansion itself, and there could be no doubt that it was the mansion, for although it had been completely hidden from the road, it was bigger than the other buildings combined.

We had come prepared for a shock, for a series of shocks. You don't buy an estate of fifty acres, a mansion, cottages and farm buildings for seven hundred and fifty pounds and expect it to look like the home of a lord or merchant prince. Certainly, this was a shock. Rarely had I seen, apart from complete ruins, anything with such an appearance of dilapidation.

The architecture of the place, if it could be called architecture, was muddled and confusing. The right-hand end of the house abutted on the wall that gave support to the cow-house, and the other farm buildings. This wall was not solid, but was arched under the buildings it supported, so that there were two cavernous shelters, each big enough to house a double-decker omnibus. Between them there were stone steps leading up to the farm building level. There was what looked like a paved courtyard between these shelters and the abutting end of the house, and there was a high stone wall, with an iron gate just below us. Could all this have been planned by the famous architect of London's original Regent Street, Carlton House Terrace, Brighton Pavilion, Buckingham Palace—John Nash?

The part of the house that joined the wall had a lower roof than the main building, and the roof of the main building had a large span sweeping down from a high ridge over what seemed an almost independent building of only two storeys. Halfway down from the ridge there was a large gap without slates, through which the rafters showed like the ribs of a decomposed corpse. Below this hole at the eaves, an iron gutter hung down from its bracket, and rested in the fork of a fair-sized ash sapling rooted in the wall itself about eight feet from ground level. The gutter obviously had acted as an automatic watering can to the roots of the tree. Here was the bulge that Eddy had referred to. It looked as though one would only have to remove one stone to have the whole wall collapse.

The children had rushed down to the gate. I shouted to them:

"Don't go near the house. It may be dangerous!"

They obediently stopped by the gate. Then Amelia cried.

"Look. There's a stream. Let's see if there are any fish in it!"

"They'll be all right down there," Clow said. "It's only shallow."

With excited shouts the three of them ran off across the field at the farther end of which was a belt of alders and sallow, and the glint of running water. Clow continued:

"This is the worst side of the mansion. The back of the place. *Jowl*, and it's not so bad as it looks!"

He waved his stick towards it.

"That wall where the tree is rooted only needs pulling down and building up straight. You could have it down and up again in no time at all. It would be a day's work only to mend the hole in the roof where the rain has been running in. Let us walk round now to the front of the mansion before going inside, and you'll see then how grand it was, and could be again."

I noted that of the many windows in the back, there was only one with unbroken panes, that the single doorway was without a door, and that the wall there, although apparently sound, was thickly grown with ivy which branched through a window cavity into the house itself. We followed Clow down the slope to the gate of the courtyard. From this point the field was comparatively level towards the tree-fringed stream, and, as we got to the end wall of the mansion, I saw that it extended for several hundred yards to the east, bounded by the stream on one side, and on the other by a continuation of the road by which we had come from Castlebridge. This road was lined with tall massive beeches, and there was another gate with big ornamental pillars facing the still, to us, hidden front of the mansion.

"It's a good field this," said Clow. "Seven acres of good clean level pasture, needing only a few tons of fertiliser to bring up the clover and the good grass. *Jowl!* If I'd had the money I'd have bought Castle Druid myself, for I'd rather be a farmer than anything else. And I've had ten years in the pits in the Rhondda Valley and three years in the South African goldmines, and two years a trawler-man fishing from Milford Haven, and I've been a fireman in a cargo steamer, and done a bit of prize-fighting, and always wanting to have a farm of my own. I've done a bit of it in my time and learnt to drive a tractor."

This was surprising and a little alarming.

"But I thought you were a mason!"

It was a tactless remark. He stopped in his stride, turned and looked at me with fiercely gleaming eyes.

"*Jowl!* It's a mason I am by damn! As good a mason as you'll find within fifty miles of this place. I'd lay bricks or stone or build a whole house for that matter with anyone. Come to my place and you'll see a cowhouse I built with my own hands, or see the roof I put on the house of Thomas Hendre, and charged him only half of what one of the town builders would have done, and a better job altogether."

I was quick to assure him that I had not meant anything disparaging by my remark, and Dain joined in:

"How wonderful having been so many things. We must come and look at your farm, and your cowhouse."

Clow smiled. The situation had been saved.

"It's not a farm, ma'am. Only a small-holding, Not big enough for a living. Now you *could* make a living

31

here."

We were at the eastern end of the house. I had been right in thinking that the roof with the hole in it extended over what was actually two joined buildings, that the back part was actually like a "lean-to", and that the bulging wall was not the main wall of the house at all. Both buildings were double-storeyed, but obviously the rooms in the main one were higher. The end wall showed no sign of decay. Both ground floor and first floor windows were intact, and while I could not see the roof, it seemed undamaged.

"This part," I said, "doesn't look too bad."

"No indeed. It's as sound as on the day it was built. But so is the front of the place, and the best thing you can do now is not to look until we've walked towards the main gate along what used to be the carriage drive, and then turn round and you'll have a fine view."

It was clear that Clow had a strong sense of the dramatic. As though engaged in a parlour game, we walked with him, with eyes front, away from the mansion for a distance of about fifty yards, then when he said "now look", we turned.

It was another shock, but this time an entirely agreeable one. Except that that there was no paint on any of the windows, the whole building looked intact, and in first-class condition. In the visible span of the roof, it seemed that there was not even a loose slate. Even the rainwater gutters were there. And there *was* architecture; not Carlton Terrace, or Regent Street, or Buckingham Palace, yet conceivably John Nash.

"I *like* it!" Dain cried. "I like it!"

"What did I tell you?" said Clow. "All it needs is the windows and door painting, and a garden in front, and a nice gravelled path up to the front door, like there was in the old days, and it would all be beautiful again and fit for the nobility to live in. You'd need a wall for the garden, and a nice gate. *Jowl!* There's nothing I would like better than to see it like that! "

It was an imposing structure. There was nothing pretentious about it, and it was not, as mansions go, formidably big, its frontage not more than eighty feet. Its height to the eaves, which had an overhang, was about twenty feet, the roof was low-pitched, and slanted from the ridge at both ends.

There were large multi-paned windows on the ground floor, shuttered from inside and evidently belonging to reception rooms; and the bedroom windows, likewise shuttered and smaller, were well-spaced. There was a columned flat-roofed portico to the front door which was central to the building. Unlike the back, which showed the naked masonry, the front was rendered with rough-cast cement which had once been lime-washed.

This was the main building. From its left end, joining it to the lower structure of the farm buildings, was that which was grown over with ivy at the back. There was no ivy here. The roof looked sound, and the window frames, although there were broken panes, seemed all right. This building in itself appeared to be a moderate-sized house, and while it did not belong architecturally to the main one, it did not detract from its agreeable aspect.

It was exciting, yet it wouldn't do to get too excited

about it yet. What lay behind those shuttered windows?

"Can we get in by the front door?" I asked Clow.

"No. It's locked and bolted from inside. We'll have to get in from the back."

We retraced our steps. As we passed round the end of the house we heard happy excited cries from the direction of the stream suggesting that the children had seen a fish or something equally interesting. The iron gate into the courtyard was off its hinges. We entered the yard. It was paved with large slabs of slate, partly hidden in a tangle of dead weeds. Through the doorless doorway we entered a large, square, low-ceilinged room with a single window looking out on to the field towards the main gate. The view was clear only through the missing panes of the window. The unbroken panes were almost opaque with dirt and cobwebs.

My first reaction as I looked round the room was one of gladness that we had not come direct to Castle Druid last night in the storm and dark. The place was almost terrifying in its squalor. The floor was hidden in an accumulation of fallen plaster on which there was a vigorous growth of grass. The plaster had fallen from the ceiling, and in places even the laths had fallen with it, revealing the bare rafters. There had been plaster on the walls too. Most of it had crumbled. There was a panelled door on the left, hanging away on one hinge. Opposite, in the darkest end of the room, was an enormous Victorian register stove, rusty and broken, and a branch of ivy with green leaves twined along the mantelshelf and up a narrow staircase with most of its steps rotted. There was a strong sickly smell of damp and decay.

"This isn't the real mansion!" said Clow defensively. "This is only the kitchen where the servants would live, and their bedrooms would be above."

We'd had a kitchen living-room in the house that we'd had built for us in Yorkshire to our own plans, and I knew that Dain must be thinking of it now. We'd planned it to be labour saving. We'd had a modern smokeless fuel cooking-range with a back boiler to give constant hot water for sink and bath. The room had been light, warm and airy, with modern oblong-paned steel-framed windows looking out back and front. We'd had linoleum on the level wooden floors and the only modern amenity we'd had to do without because of our isolated site was electricity.

There was no sign of a sink here. In spite of the smell of damp there was no sign of piped water, although I recalled that the vendor had told us that there was a good water supply to farm and house. But it was the vegetation growing from the floor that bothered me most.

"Is it an earth floor?" I asked.

"Earth? No, by damn! The grass is growing on it only because of the sand and lime in the fallen plaster, and with the rain driving through the doorway." He poked his stick into the rubble. "No one has lived in this place since Christmas Morgan died, more than twenty years ago. He had it rented for this part only and the farm, although he was supposed to look after the big house.

"Christmas was all right until his wife died of the cancer. Then he took to the bottle and never did another stroke of work. There was little money in farming then anyway, just after the first war. He got into debt, and his stock and implements and then his furniture were sold up. A sad misery he was, with only his bed and a chair or two for furniture, and often I'd come in here and see him, and bring him a bite to eat, and make a fire for him if the weather was cold, for he'd be too drunk to light it himself. He'd been a chapel man before his wife died, and she'd been a singer in the choir, but he'd turned atheist, and he'd have nothing to do with the pastor who came to try and console him. He never washed, and never shaved or had his hair cut. He looked like a tramp, and the children would run away from him if they saw him outside the house, for he had a wild look in his eyes too. But I'll not tell you now how he finished it all. When he'd gone, the people who owned the place wouldn't let it again, or *Jowl,* I'd have taken it myself. They wanted to sell it at a big price, but the land had all gone back, and no one would have it. Look now at the floor. It's all tiled. There's nothing wrong with that."

He had scraped some of the debris away with the side of his foot revealing beneath it an area of red brick tiles, each about six inches square, well set and level. Dain cried excitedly:

"How lovely! Think how they'll look when they're scrubbed and polished. If we got a new cooking-stove, and did the walls and the ceiling, and mended the window and the door, this could be a perfect living-room. If we had the ceiling whitewashed, and the walls distempered pale pink, it would be quite light and cheerful."

Clow actually laughed.

"*Jowl*, that's the spirit ma'am! If I had my shovel here and a wheelbarrow, I'd have the floor clear for you in half an hour. Come on now and let us see the rest of the place."

"Where is the water supply?" I asked.

"I'll show you that later. There's a well up near the motor road, nice clean water and cool, but the pipes that brought it to the yard have rusted away. It will be easy enough putting new ones in."

The panelled door led into a long corridor, paved with slate slabs similar to those of the courtyard. They were tolerably clear of debris. The plastered ceiling, although cracked and hung with cobwebs, seemed mainly sound. On the right, the wall, also sound, was unbroken by windows or doors, but on the left were four small rooms. The first had a window facing the courtyard, and it was fitted with wide slate shelves, their ends let into the walls.

"The dairy and pantry," said Clow. "And I wish it was mine. There's nothing better than slate slabs for keeping your pans of milk cool in hot weather."

"It's grand," said Dain. "And so handy for the kitchen. The shelves will look lovely when they're scrubbed, and the walls and ceiling are whitewashed. A real dairy. Can't you see the bowls of milk and cream and pats of butter?"

I could, but before we had milk and cream and butter we had to have cows and food to feed them with, and before we could do that we had many, many things to do. There was little wrong with the dairy except its dirt and that the window frame looked rotten. But when we got

37

to the next room which was of similar shape and size, I had a shock. The flagged floor, and three of the walls were all right. The fourth wall, whose window frame was completely missing, was leaning outwards, and there were gaps between it and the partition walls. The ends of the ceiling rafters were hanging loose, and the ceiling and obviously the floor of the room above had a dangerous slant. The leaning wall dripped with moisture. Clow, however, was quite unperturbed.

"This is the inside of the wall that's got to be rebuilt. The ceiling and the floors of the rooms above can be levelled up when the wall is put right, only you'll need a few planks where the rain has got in and caused a bit of rot."

"It might make a good bathroom," Dain said, not quite so enthusiastically as before, "when the wall is mended."

"Funny you should say that, ma'am. The bathroom was in the room above this, but Christmas sold the bath to someone for a water trough, and all the lead pipes to a tinker, to get money for his whisky. There was a water closet too, and one in the room next door to this, but they've gone. The mansion was one of the first houses in Pembrokeshire to have a water closet. Only the nobility would have such things in those days."

We moved on. The room next door, which was smaller, showed signs of having once justified this rather peculiar mark of nobility and fame. But the device itself and the plumbing were missing. As in the previous room the outer wall was leaning out, and the ceiling was aslant.

"Are the drains still in place?" I asked.

"Why not indeed? Christmas couldn't pull them up and sell them. We'll find them if we dig for them. They'll lead down the meadow, and there was a pit, but it will have been filled in with the soil."

The fourth room was the same size as the second, and in similar condition except that the outer wall had less bulge, and the ceiling less slant. We had come to the end of the corridor. There was a big panelled door that was shut.

"Now we'll see the real mansion," Clow said. "All this was for the servants only. Now you'll see how grand the place was."

He opened the door. Its hinges creaked, but they appeared to be unbroken. We entered a large, lofty hall which extended lengthways at right angles to the corridor, and through the house to the front entrance door, and it was illuminated by a handsome fanlight above the door itself. Its ceiling was arched and there was a moulded frieze. Opposite to the front door was the approach to a superb curving staircase, with white marble steps, a wrought iron and fluted mahogany railed balustrade leading to the first floor.

There was no sign of decay here. The floor of the hall was hardwood, and looked as though it had been polished. The stairs were in two flights, divided by a landing. Here was a tall, vertically narrow window with its panes intact, and in the wall nearby was an arched niche, which looked as though it had once contained statuary.

This was getting exciting. There were three "room"

doorways leading from the hall. Clow entered the first, the one nearest to the staircase, and he opened the folding wooden shutters of the single window, which looked out over the field towards the stream.

It was a handsome room, almost square in shape, about twenty feet each way. The ceiling was the same height as the other rooms we had seen, for we were still outside the main building, still in what I judged to be a lateral extension of it. Yet there was no bulge or even cracks in the wall. The ceiling was beautifully moulded with a centre circular pattern from which there probably once hung a glass candelabra. The walls, painted a dingy green, were panelled waist high, and in the wall on the left was a large, unmistakably Regency, drawing-room fireplace, with white marble surrounds and mantelshelf. The floor, like that of the hall, was oak, and sound.

"What a beautiful room!" Dain cried, "and it doesn't need much doing to it."

I sounded the panelling.

"This seems all right. We ought to scrape the paint off, and have the bare wood."

"Yes. And wax it. It will look lovely. And the walls and ceiling ivory distemper!"

"This was the library in the old days," said Clow. "And there's not much wrong with it, is there? A nice warm place it could be with a roaring fire in the grate. There are two other rooms downstairs, one bigger than this , and one smaller. But the small one has its ceiling down."

We moved into the bigger one first, and this time Dain helped me to unfasten the shutters of one of the two windows while Clow did the other, and she said:

"It's wonderful having shutters. Think what they'll save in black-out blinds. Isn't it all exciting? I think we ought to move in as soon as the furniture comes. We can easily live in two rooms at first, and look, this one's just as good as the other."

It *was*. Il was the same shape, and its greater size was balanced by the second window which, like the kitchen window, faced the main gate. The ceiling was higher and some of the moulding had broken away. One of the jambs of the fireplace too was leaning out, but the fireplace, itself slightly bigger than that of the library and of different design, was another Regency gem.

Clow was beaming.

"A nice room, eh? I thought you'd like it. Think what it would have been in the old days with thick carpets on the floor, and rich curtains and furniture, and pictures on the wall and costly ornaments on the mantelshelf. *Jowl!* If Squire Vaughan had taken my great-grandmother to church all this might have been mine.

"My grandfather Llewellyn wouldn't have gambled the estate away if it had come to him. A good, sober man he was by all accounts, and my father was the same. He worked at the slate quarry here when I was a boy. He was a big, strong man, very stern and religious, and very free with the stick. I tried to run away to sea when I was thirteen, but when I got to Cardiff I couldn't get a ship, so I went into the pits, and I was always too afraid of the old man to go back. My young sister Rosie ran away from him too. Wanted to go on the stage. A beautiful girl with hair the colour of bright gold. She did well for herself, but not on the stage. She married a Canadian she met in London, and went to live in Winnipeg. He was a corn merchant and made a lot of money in the first war. But all three of their sons were killed in the fighting. They live in Vancouver now. Every Christmas I get a letter from her and a parcel. Let us get on now to the other rooms."

As we moved into the hall again I took a sideways glance at Clow. He was wearing heavy workman's boots, corduroy trousers, a rather shabby serge jacket, with a cotton scarf knotted at his neck, an old felt hat. His hands were gnarled, the nails broken. Yet there was something about his bearing and manner, quite apart from what he had told us, that convinced me that his story was true, and it was easy for me to picture him in a well-cut tweed suit, handmade shoes, laundered shirt with collar and tie, the garb of a country gentleman at home; gold cufflinks, a gold signet ring on a well-manicured hand, a deerstalker hat on his head, his moustache neatly trimmed, his teeth cared for, smoking expensive tobacco in an expensive pipe, speaking with the accent and manner of an officer in the guards, a member of an exclusive London club.

Was he resentful, jealous, of our owning Castle Druid? Was his enthusiasm for the place unbiased? I could not believe that he was merely job hunting. I still liked him, but I was still rather afraid of him.

There was a third door almost opposite that of the big room. He opened it, walked in and opened the shutters of a single window facing the main gate. We followed, stopping at the threshold, and we had another shock, again of mixed dismay and delight.

On the floor of the room was another heap of fallen plaster. Above it the ceiling was split along the middle, with the fractured ends of the joists hanging down at least a foot from the level. On the right-hand wall, that facing the window, a large patch of plaster had fallen away down to the wainscoting which in parts was rotted. The fireplace was Victorian and hideous; the surrounds and mantelshelf, although possibly white marble, had been painted over with the same dingy brown that had been used on the wainscoting of the other room, and there was another patch of fallen plaster above the mantelshelf. And yet, looking round, I thought that it was one of the most exciting rooms I had ever seen, and I knew that Dain was thinking the same. It was unique.

It was square, like the other two, but considerably smaller. The doorway wall, however, was curved, with the doorway central. The door, itself panelled, and an exquisite piece of joinery, was also curved, and on each side of it, following the curve, were built-in cupboards. The doors of these were glazed, and miraculously none of the panes was even cracked. The shelves were narrow and clearly designed to hold silver and bric-à-brac. From the lintel of the doorway, the plastered wall was scalloped to meet the moulding of the actual ceiling. And this moulding had not been involved in the collapse of the ceiling.

"This," I said, "is the best yet. The fireplace looks wrong but we could change it with the one in the library. I'm certain this room was designed by Nash. The curved wall and cupboards! Even the glass in the cupboard doors is curved. How lucky they're not broken. We could never replace them!"

"It could be made to look heavenly!" cried Dain.

"Even the ceiling doesn't look hopeless," I said.

"You could mend that with plasterboard," said Clow. "Pull down the old plaster and brace up the joists, and nail plaster board straight on to them, and it would be as good as new. I knew you'd like this. Let us go upstairs now and see the bedrooms. Four of them and the bathroom will need repairs, but most of them are all right and would need only painting."

"I hope the children are all right," Dain said as we moved towards the staircase. "Don't you think we ought to find out what they're doing? They may be in mischief."

"They'll be all right," said Clow. "And safer down there by the stream and quarry than in the house, for some parts of it are dangerous. I wouldn't let them be in this room until the ceiling is mended, and then there's part of the balustrade gone at the top of the staircase, and it's nearly a fifteen foot drop to below."

When we reached the top of the first flight of stairs, I saw that on the upper landing two of the ornamental posts and part of the horizontal rail were broken off, leaving a dangerous gap, and I said:

"Yes. We'll have to fix a board or something across that before we have the children here."

Clow had suddenly stopped, and he looked at the gap.

"Perhaps," he said, "you'd better know now why the thing is broken like that, for someone else may tell you or the little ones, and they might be frightened, although it happened a long time ago. This is where poor Christmas put an end to his misery. He put a cow-halter round his neck, tied one end to the rail and jumped. The rail gave way, but he'd given himself the right drop, and couldn't have done it better if he'd been hanged in gaol on the gallows!"

Dain gave a gasp of horror. I was horrified myself, yet Clow's statement had been so vivid, so clear in its "essential" detail, so matter of fact, that all I could say was:

"How awful. We must certainly mend the balustrade, and not let the children know what happened."

"*Ody, ody*," Clow said. "There's an old hayrack up in the stable would do for the time being. In a way it's a good thing Christmas did it in the house, for it's kept many people away who might have damaged the place. Here's the first bedroom on the left. Wait till I have opened the shutters."

There were four good-sized bedrooms in the main building of the mansion: one above the big reception room, and the one with the cracked ceiling, two more above the library in the wing. Whether the grim episode Clow had described had acted as a deterrent to potential house-wreckers or not, it was a fact that these rooms had suffered very little damage. With their floors swept and scrubbed, and the cobwebs brushed from ceilings and walls and windows, they were all habitable. But the rooms that were on the side of the house with the bulging wall (there were four, corresponding with the ones on the ground floor) were in a dangerous state with their joists loose from the wall, and floors aslant. The bath-less bathroom was one of them. In that the ceiling too was gone, and through it I could see the roof and daylight in the gap where the slates had fallen off.

A long passage, which corresponded to the flagged one on the ground floor, led to the servants' quarters above the kitchen. Here were four more smaller rooms, shut off from the passage by what had been a thick, felt-padded door. And there was the broken staircase down to the kitchen itself. There were broken windows, fallen plaster in all these rooms. The ivy, climbing up the staircase, extended over the ceiling of one of them. Yet all the floors seemed sound. There was nothing here which in normal times an ordinary builder, or amateurs like ourselves, could not put right. But these were not normal times. There was, to use the current phrase, "a war on".

We had stopped in one of the bedrooms whose broken window looked out across the meadow to the stream which presumably our children were still exploring. Clow said:

"Well, you've seen all of the mansion now. What do you make of it?"

"It's much better than I expected," I said. "But there's going to be a lot to do, perhaps more than we did expect. We can do a lot ourselves, but we're going to need help. What do you feel about it? We're not rich," I added.

Again Clow gave me that shrewd look.

"Listen," he said. "If you had one of the town contractors to put all this right he'd charge at least a thousand pounds for the job, and then it would be no better than I could do it with my own hands. But there's not a town contractor could take it on at present if you offered him twice as much. *Jowl*, they're all too busy building factories, camps and aerodromes and the like for the Government, and making great fortunes for themselves. I could be earning twelve pounds a week if I took a job with one of them, mason or bricklayer. But I'll be my own boss or nothing, by damn. To hell with them all. If I worked for you it would be because I'd like to see the old place look beautiful again.

"Listen. I'll tell you what I'll do. I'll work on the place for three shillings and sixpence an hour, and you find all the material except the slates and stone and timber in the old quarry. Cement and lime mortar, and nails and the like, and plasterboard. All those things you can buy from Eddy Jones. He's got everything for the building trade in his shop and timber-yard. Three and sixpence an hour I'll want, work every day except Saturday afternoon and the Sabbath, from eight o'clock until it's dark, and maybe after dark too if you have lamps, for there'll be plenty of work to do inside. But I'll not want to be kept waiting for my money. I'll want it every Saturday dinnertime. And if we don't get on well together then we'll say so, and you'll get someone else for the job. I'm my own boss, remember. I'll not do anything I don't want to do even for ten pounds an hour. So you must take it or leave it."

I was still afraid of him. There was something verging on truculence in his manner. And yet if there was one thing I admired in a man it was self-confidence, and independence. He had a good measure of both. He was going to be difficult I imagined. We'd have to be very tactful with him, avoid treading on his corns. But I could see that Dain had summed him up, was liking him, and

47

I said:

"Right. I agree to that," and I added, tactfully, "What do you think we ought to do first? We want to live in the place as soon as possible."

I could see that I was taking the right line with him. He was smiling.

"First? The first job's the roof. Get the slates back. Then the wall. I'll want four straight oak posts cutting from the wood to hold up the floor joists and the wall plate under the eaves. Then we'll have the wall down and get it built up again. But we'll not be able to start the roof today. There'll be the slates to bring from the quarry. I tell you what I will do now. I'll go home. I've got a hand-barrow and a wheelbarrow which I can put on it. If you want to get into the place soon we can get the kitchen cleared. You'll need fires on. I expect most of the chimneys will be blocked up with old jackdaws' nests. I'll bring ladders and shovels too. Let us go downstairs now by the way we've come. You'll soon be settled in, don't worry."

As we moved to go I heard voices. Leaning out through the broken window I saw the children running up the pasture from the stream. Amelia and Jane had something in their hands.

We hurried down, and, with some difficulty, Clow opened the door, and Dain and I went to meet them.

Their faces were red, their eyes shining with excitement. The objects that Amelia and Jane were carrying were small slates, and Angus also was carrying one, but this a larger one. Words tumbled from them.

"It's a wonderful stream. We've seen millions of fish!"

"We've seen a huge eel. We nearly caught it."

"There's a little house. There's millions of slates like these. We've brought these to mend the roof."

"We could see the place where the lake has been. Do let's build a wall across the stream and make the lake again. We could have a boat."

"We'd have caught the eel if it hadn't been so slippery, but we know where it went. We could set a line for it. Do come and look at the stream."

"Is the house all right? Can we go into it now? How soon can we come to live in it?"

"Oh! do come and see the stream and the little house."

Clow had joined us and he was still smiling.

"Ah, they're a healthy brood of youngsters you've got. And I see they've found the slates. We'll want maybe a hundred of them for the job. And there's plenty of good timber lying about in the quarry. But I wouldn't take the children into the house yet. Go down and look at the stream and the quarry, and as soon as I'm back we'll make a start on the kitchen. There's plenty of firewood down there too. And that will do until you get some coal. We'll soon have the place safe and comfortable."

"Right," I said. And to the children: "Come on, kids, we'll go look at your millions of fish. Come on!"

Leaving Clow to walk more sedately towards the main gate, we all joined hands and ran helter-skelter down to the stream.

3

There was indeed "a war on", and at that period things were looking anything but bright for Britain and her allies. The enemy, and the enemy now included Italy, Rumania, Bulgaria, Finland, with Japan signed-up, but not yet quite ready to pounce, occupied the whole of the Atlantic seaboard with the exception of Portugal and Spain. Yugoslavia and Greece had been invaded. Our forces in North Africa, weakened by withdrawals for the desperate defence of Greece, had been obliged to yield hard-won ground to the combined German and Italian armies under Rommel. Egypt and its vital Canal were threatened. And now the enemy was sweeping into Russia.

In the air things were going more in our favour. The Battle of Britain had been fought and won, although at very great cost. The night raids on our cities and ports had become less severe as our attacks on Germany had increased in frequency and strength. But at sea, with the enemy's U-boats, surface raiders and land-based aircraft doing their utmost to disrupt Britain's supplies of food, oil, munitions, and raw materials for her factories, some of which supplies were being diverted to help Russia by an especially hazardous route, it was a grim unrelenting battle.

As I had told Eddy Jones, I had served with the Air Force in the Kaiser's War, and was debarred from taking a fighting part in this one. I hadn't, since the War had started, been able to get on with my ordinary writing. I had written a "straight" book on the part that British fishermen were taking in the mine-sweeping service. But the thing I had wanted to do, for it had seemed most worthwhile, was to reclaim the forty-odd neglected acres of the farm we had bought cheaply some years before and produce food. In this circumstances had thwarted us. The land we had cleared and started to cultivate was now being torn up for the more precious silica rock that lay beneath the soil. Then, miraculously had come the offer of Castle Druid, for which we had to put down only £250 of the £750 — the balance on a three-year mortgage.

It was not only as a home and a reclaimable farm that it had appealed to us so strongly. We both liked children, and, for Dain, at least, the more the merrier. We believed that even in peacetime, it was better for children to grow up in the country rather than in towns. Adder Howe, our Yorkshire house, had been barely big enough for our own family. It had looked as though Castle Druid, when it had been put in order, would make it possible for us to take in some evacuee children, and perhaps fulfil another of Dain's dreams, to run a sort of school and try out some of her own theories about education — one of them being that the slummiest of young children, given the right food, the right environment, and the companionship of children whose early lives had been better favoured, would respond as beneficially as plants moved from poor soil to a good one. The Nazis had proved how this could be done the wrong way round.

It was not going to be easy. These were the days of growing austerity, of scarcities and controls. All private domestic building had been virtually banned. You could not buy any building materials, timber or bricks or cement without a permit, and even then only in strictly-limited quantities. If prices were officially controlled, they were also well above pre-war figures. Our capital was small.

Our first job must be to make the house weather-tight and safe; to clear and clean and repair enough of its rooms for us to move in. The children were going to be a problem until this was done. Amy suggested a solution.

"Why, let them go to the village school, for Mano is the headmistress of it. She'll teach them the Welsh, as she teaches the Welsh children the English, and they'll be happy there, for there's plenty of singing and dancing too. They'll get a good dinner and free milk under the new law, and we can look after the little one while you are putting things straight at the mansion. I'll come and give you a help there myself when I have got my own work done."

Amelia and Jane took kindly to the suggestion. Angus, who hadn't yet been to school, seemed a little apprehensive, but after breakfast the three of them set off down the main street, Angus between his sisters gripping their hands tightly. Tom had offered to run us out to Castle Druid again, but I had protested, and we were arguing about it when Eddy Jones drew up in his shooting-brake, and settled the matter. I had rung him up last night telling him that we had been round the mansion, and that Clow had advised us to approach him about cement and other materials. How should we set about getting the permits? He'd promised to come out and see us at the first chance.

He was dead sober, but as high-spirited and agreeable as he had been on his birthday. He was sorry that he had missed seeing the elder children. He produced some chocolate from his pocket for Timothy.

"What do you think of our friends at the Jew's Harp?" he said as we drove out of the village. "You'd have to go a long way to find a kinder lot of people, eh? And hard-working too. The pub and the farm were in a poor way when they took it over on a mortgage just after the end of the first war. The man who had it then was drinking hard and the pub nearly lost its licence. Old Dai Evans, their father, had spent most of his life in the pits. He'd got miner's silicosis and he died soon after he'd come back to Castlebridge, and it was the old lady and the daughters and Tom who paid off the mortgage. Poor Sara. She got married, but her man was killed at Gallipoli, and her baby was born dead and she's never quite recovered, and sometimes she'll have a fit of crying and the old lady will have to comfort her just as if she was a little girl."

"Poor thing," said Dain feelingly. "How sad that her baby died too."

"Yes. But she's happy enough when she's singing. There's nothing like music for cheering you up when you're sad. And what do you make of Clow? He's a queer customer, isn't he?"

I said that we liked him, and that so far we had got

on very well with him.

Eddy laughed.

"He's all right if you keep on the right side of him. He's a first-class workman, but very self-opinionated. A thing has got to be done his way, or he'll not do it at all. That's no good for an employer, but apart from that I wish I had half a dozen men like him."

"Is it true what he says about being the descendant of one of the squires of Castle Druid?"

"Yes indeed. He's no liar."

We drew up at the gate near the cottages. As I opened the gate Eddy exclaimed,

"My, it's a beautiful place this! Beautiful. It's a long time since I was out here. Tell me now, how much of the land is yours?"

Yesterday we had been too concerned with seeing the mansion to bother about the land, and after we had gone with the children to see the stream and the quarry and the things that they had discovered, there had been no time to walk the boundaries. But these were marked on the map that had accompanied the purchase deed, and from the gateway the extent of them was generally clear.

The stream made a rough half circle. On our left, falling gently from the hills, it was partly hidden by a wood through which our boundary ran. The wood narrowed into sparse clumps of alder where the stream was bordered by the meadow and broadened again at the slate quarry. On the opposite side of the stream the land rose steeply, and its banks were covered with bramble and furze with outcrops of bare rock, almost to the same level as that of our present viewpoint. Then it levelled into what was virtually a plateau, and there were fields divided by thick walls and thorn hedges reaching to the right and left, five in all. Two of them were as green as the pasture. The others seemed to be almost entirely grown over with bracken, and beyond them and our boundary was unfenced land with bracken, patched with the dark brown of heather, which again gave way to the bleached green of moorland grass as it rose to the high hills.

I answered Eddy's question, pointing out the boundaries.

He was silent for a moment, then he said practically:

"You're going to have your work cut out bringing those fields into cultivation. I'm not a farmer though. You'd certainly be able to graze some stock here, and keep a cow or two. But let's see the mansion, and what it is you'll need from me."

We moved down until we were in sight of it, and there was Clow up on the roof, working at the hole. A ladder reached to the eaves, a light roof-ladder was hooked on to the ridge. He had already reduced the size of the hole by nearly half with the quarry slates. Near the foot of the ladder were three heavy oak saplings, which he must have cut and carried from the wood.

We shouted "Good morning" to him. He half turned, nodded his head slightly, the gesture almost of a dictator acknowledging the cheers of a mob, and without speaking, went on with his job.

We carried on, and stopped again near the ladder. Eddy gave us a wink, and then spoke to Clow in Welsh.

Clow didn't turn, but he muttered an answer in Welsh, and then in English he said,

"Go and look at the kitchen now, and I'll come down when I've got this row of slates fixed."

There was a huge pile of debris outside the kitchen doorway, and another pile of ivy branches. We went in. We had started on the clearance of this room yesterday afternoon, but hadn't made much headway when Tom had come to take us back. Now it was completely transformed. All the loose plaster had been cleared from the ceiling and walls, the ivy branches pulled out, the floor itself swept clear, showing all the red tiles. The broken staircase was still as it had been. So was the fireplace. But the window was cleared, there was plenty of light in the room. Even the musty smell seemed less noticeable.

"Clow is a marvel, isn't he?" said Dain enthusiastically, and to Eddy: "I wish you'd seen what this was like yesterday!"

"He's a worker, yes," Eddy answered, a little peevishly I thought. "I told you he was. But he needn't give himself such airs. And he's got no manners. This doesn't look bad. What about the stove though? That one looks as though its day is over."

"We were hoping," I said, "to get a modern range with a back boiler for bath water and kitchen sink, to burn anthracite or coke. But there's no water supply to the place at present. There's a spring, but the pipes have gone. There's no bath, no sanitation."

Eddy whistled.

"You're not going to get a new stove these days, nor

a bath, or sinks, or lavatory bowls or anything like that. All supplies from the manufacturers have stopped long ago. Isn't there any plumbing at all left in the house?

"None," I said.

"Oh dear! That's bad. It's a terrible job getting hold of piping. All the lead is needed for making bullets. Your only hope is to get hold of some second-hand stuff."

"We don't object to second-hand material," I said quickly, "or third-hand for that matter!" And I told him how in our first home in Cornwall we had equipped our kitchen and bathroom with the stove and sink and bath and other apparatus that had been saved from a wrecked yacht; that even in the house we'd had built for us in Yorkshire we'd economised by using second-hand doors, and there had been no war-time restrictions when we'd had it built. Also that we had done quite a lot of the carpentering ourselves.

"It's far more fun!" said Dain.

"I wish my wife thought the same way," Eddy said a little wryly. "She's all for having everything new and posh. Well, maybe I can lay hands on something that would suit you. I know every builder's yard in the district. As a matter of fact I think there's a cooking-stove in one of my own sheds, unless it's been collected by the scrap-iron merchant. It came from a house which had electricity put in just before the war. Only it hasn't a boiler. You could get over that by having an independent stove and boiler, one of the slow-burning sort. They're very economical, and I might get hold of one of those second-hand, and perhaps a cylinder and service tank, and enough second-hand galvanised piping for your job.

I'm curious to see the whole place. Do you mind if we have a walk round?"

We started a tour of the mansion. The weather was still fine. We had left all the shutters folded back, and where possible had opened the windows. The smell of decay was there, but less strong than it had been yesterday. Eddy didn't say much. He stamped on the floors of the three reception rooms, and said that he agreed with me that they were quite sound. He liked what we had called the John Nash room, and said that it ought to be very nice when the ceiling was mended. He admired the staircase. Clow had fixed the section of hayrack across the broken balustrade. I asked Eddy if he had heard about Christmas Morgan and how he had hanged himself here.

I thought that he looked a little uncomfortable.

"Yes, indeed. I've heard about Christmas Morgan, but I didn't know that this was the very place where he did it. Well, well!"

I could not resist repeating what Clow had told us and I pointed to the fractured post to which the halter had been tied.

"Well, well," he repeated. "Fancy that now. It must have been a nasty sight for those who found him. But I don't believe in ghosts. Do you?"

I assured him, not without some reservations, that we did not, and that we preferred to face the facts of life and death.

"I'd believe in a ghost if I saw one," I said.

He stared down the well of the staircase into which Christmas had taken his fatal leap, and I fancied that he shuddered.

"Yes, yes indeed. Come on now. Let us see the rest of the house."

When we got back to the kitchen, Clow was waiting for us. There was a subtle hostility in the way he looked at Eddy, who smiled at him urbanely.

"We've been having a look round the old place, Clow," he said. "There's going to be a lot to do to put it right, but it's not so bad as I thought it would be."

"There's nothing wrong about it," Claw growled, "that can't be put right, easy enough. And I can do it."

Eddy remained unruffled.

"There's no one could do it better. But what material will you need?"

"*Jowl!* That depends on what you've got, and whether the damned Government allows you to sell it. Is mortar on the ration now?"

Eddy grinned.

"We have lime mortar, ready-mixed in the machine. Cement is scarce, but I can let you have a couple of bags. I'm hoping you won't want timber though. It's as scarce as butter. All that we've got is unseasoned oak and elm and it's all requisitioned for the Docks at Milford Haven."

Clow looked impatient.

"It's only for the rotted floors and joists, and the window frames we need timber. There's enough logs down in the quarry for all we need, if you can saw it at your mill. Go and look at it, for I want to get on with the roof. When that's done I have the wall to pull down and build again. I'll need two tons of your mortar for that job."

He turned to go.

"Can you let us have glass for the windows?" I asked Eddy. "And putty?" adding, as Clow was already out of hearing, "I'll be doing that job myself."

He winked.

"You measure the panes, and I'll have them all cut for you, and send them out with the mortar. I haven't much time now but I'd like to go down and see your quarry, and the timber he's talking about. It's years since I've been out here. There used to be trout in that stream."

Clow was already climbing back to the roof with a load of slates under one arm.

We walked down to the stream. Almost opposite to the mansion there was a wide depression in the valley, which narrowed sharply on the right, where a massive wall of un-cemented stone and earth reached from each bank, with a broken gap through which the stream ran. The wall continued as a retaining wall to the meadow itself for about a hundred yards upstream, gradually diminishing and then petering out into a low grassy bank. The bank of the opposite side was mostly bare rock.

There could be no doubt that the depression had once been the bed of the lake. It was grown over with brambles und thorn and sallow.

"Did you ever see the lake?" I asked Eddy.

"No. It was before my time. But it must have looked pretty and big too. Why if it had been up to the level of the wall there, there must have been nearly an acre of it. Big enough to sail a boat on, eh? Have you thought of rebuilding the dam wall, and having the lake back?"

Had we indeed! When we had read the first detailed description of Castle Druid one of the things that had excited us most was that it had a stream, and that there had once been a lake. But we had resolved then that the remaking of the lake, unless it was going to be a simple and cheap job, must take a low place on our list of priorities.

I told Eddy about this resolution. We moved along to the broken wall. The gap through which the stream ran was about fourteen feet across, and the depth from the wall top at least twelve feet. At its lowest point there must have been thickness of wall and rubble of ten feet, but this would have been tapered as it rose. The children on their first exciting exploration yesterday had piled some stones and loose sods across the stream in the gap, and had formed quite a large pool, and in this pool we caught the flash of a small trout. Clearly, Eddy was not going to take my resolution seriously.

"You know it wouldn't be a very big job filling in that gap," he said. "You'd have to divert the stream first, then make a culvert, and build on top of it and close the culvert when the wall is finished. Get all the bushes and whatnot cleared out of the bed first. Man, it would be great fun watching the water getting higher and higher."

"It *would* be exciting!" cried Dain.

"Stop it!" I protested. "I know all that. And in case Eddy is going to tell me, I also know that if we make the lake the small trout in the stream will grow fat and multiply. And I also know that even without the lake, there's enough volume of water in the stream to work a waterwheel, and that at a farm a little lower down the stream there is a disused waterwheel that we'd probably be able to buy.

"Get thee behind me Satan! We've got to make the house habitable, and repair the farm buildings. We've also got to clear and plough up the land, and mend all the fences. We mustn't think about lakes and trout and waterwheels. Let's push on to the quarry and see the wood."

Eddy laughed. We crossed the stream just below the gap. On the other side was a fairly wide path, marked now with the ruts of Clow's wheelbarrow, which led shortly to the quarry.

No wonder that the children had been excited about it. It was a fascinating place. The quarry was carved out of the steep bank which rose to our top fields. Clow had told us that, although the slates were good quality, the beds from which they came were at an awkward angle. He had explained that the first process in quarrying was to get out thick slabs of the rock. These were trimmed square, and then split with thin wedges along the lines of lamination. The quarry must have been opened first by the builders of the mansion for building stone for which the unsplit blocks were equally suitable. The squires had never tried to run it for commercial purposes, but only for the estate. After the First World War a company had been formed to lease the quarry. The company had gone bankrupt during the slump.

The face of the quarry was not dangerously steep. The overburden of mixed soil and rock had been spread out to the edge of the stream to form a space as large and level as a tennis court. On this was an open shed with a corrugated iron roof. It was a perfect place for the children to play in in rainy weather. In it was a long wide workshop bench. There were stacks of dressed slates of various sizes. And there was a pile of sawn logs, some measuring eighteen feet, a foot wide and six inches thick, which I had already examined and found to be Columbian pine, and completely free from rot.

Eddy whistled when he saw them.

"Man, you're in luck. You couldn't get hold of stuff like this these days for love or money. If there's more here than you want, I'll give you a good price for it."

"I'll remember that," I said cautiously. "I can't tell yet how much we shall want. Could you saw some of it into boards and sizes for window frames?"

"Certainly. You tell me the sizes and I'll do the rest. We've got a planing machine too. This stuff would work up very nice. There'll be a road into the quarry from the main road. A lorry could easily pick this up. My, you're in luck. But if I owned this place I'd never rest till I'd had a crack at filling up the dam wall. I must have another look at it on our way back."

"Eddy, *bach*, S̓atan!" I said. "*I* think we ought to look at the quarry track and make certain your lorry can do it, and go back to the mansion that way. Stop tempting me about the lake."

4

AMY AND SARA had lent us sweeping and scrubbing brushes, buckets and a large kettle. They had also given us food and a bottle of milk. When we got back to the house—Eddy had left us at the top gate after we had surveyed the quarry road and found it passable for his lorry—we started work on the kitchen.

The oven and side boiler of the range were broken, but the grate seemed all right for temporary use. It was filled with twigs and straw, and this debris extended up the flue, and was evidently the product of many generations of nesting jackdaws. Poking up the flue with a broom shaft I dislodged it, and looking up saw daylight. The twigs were dry, making a first-rate kindling, and there was plenty of more substantial fuel in the broken staircase. There was a good draught. Soon we had our first fire going, and the kettle on for hot water.

I had an idea that, like most British workmen, Clow wouldn't like to be watched while he was at work, but also guessed that he was susceptible to praise and even flattery. We could hear him, working on the roof, and occasionally I heard him mutter the word *jowl* when apparently something had gone wrong, but I resisted the temptation to walk outside and see how the job was proceeding.

We had plenty to do. While Dain set about sweeping the floor, I started to clean the old putty from the broken windows. Eddy had promised to send out the lime and cement and the cut panes after dinnertime, and his lorry would collect the timber. It wasn't long, however, before Clow came to the kitchen doorway, still without a door, and there was something in his manner suggestive of a boy who had done something rather clever, eager for admiration.

"Come now and see the roof," he said.

We went out and looked at it, standing back from the bulging wall. He had completely filled in the gap where the rafters had been showing, and it was only by the colour of the unweathered slates that one could tell where the gap had been.

"You've made a fine job of it!" I said with sincere enthusiasm.

He was grinning.

"Yes, indeed," he agreed. "You'll not find a drop of water coming through that now. And *jowl*, if you had had the town contractors to do it they wouldn't have had their ladders up to it yet—and there would have been at least three men getting in each other's way. Now I'll need a little help for the next job, to hold the posts while I pin them under the rafters. We'll do that from the inside. I'll tell you when I need the help."

It did not bother me that Clow seemed to be assuming command of operations, that he was going to regard me as a sort of plumber's mate. In spite of his bragging, I was convinced more than ever of his technical ability, his almost feverish zest for work. Already he had picked up one of the heavy oak saplings, and was pushing it through one of the paneless windows below the bulging wall. He refused my immediate help.

"Get on with your own job," he said. "I'll shout when I want you."

I would not have had the courage to tackle that wall myself. I should not have known where to begin. The bulge extended for at least fifteen feet and was at least two feet from the vertical at its most dangerous point, midway between the ground and the eaves. When Clow at last shouted for me from the room next to the pantry (he had got in through the window) I found that he had cleared some of the rotted floorboards from the ceiling close to the wall, so that I could see the rafters of the room above. Two of the oak posts were reaching up to the rafters but not quite touching them, and they were still loose.

"Listen," he said, or rather ordered, "I'm going upstairs now. I have a batten to lay under the ends of the rafters, to spread the weight, and you must hold the posts upright and steady while I wedge them in. Don't worry if a bit of plaster falls from above. The roof will lift a bit but the wall won't move until I'm ready."

It *had* occurred to me that the wall, and roof too, might collapse. Close to where I stood, there was a gap of several inches between the main wall and that of the partition between this and the next room. The stones still dripped with moisture. It looked as though one had only to give a little push anywhere to have the whole thing tumbling down. Once more I had to assume my fatalistic optimism. I was not going to let Clow see that I was scared.

He picked up a sledge hammer and left me. I heard him walking up the staircase and along the top landing and then on the floor of the room immediately above me, which, with its joist ends loose from the outer wall, sagged perilously with his weight. Then I saw him through the gap in the floor that he had made. He was straddling the gap and he had in his hands a thick plank which now he held up to the rafters.

"Let's have the first post now. Hold it up straight."

I obeyed orders.

Holding the board with one hand against the rafters, he pushed the top end of the post against it until it was lightly jammed. Then with the sledge hammer, he tapped it tighter, and a shower of dust descended on to my head, nearly blinding me.

"That's nice," Clow shouted. "Now for the next post."

I groped for it, not daring to look up again. He moved its top end into position, and repeated the wedging process. There was a further cascade of dust, but nothing more solid fell. The post was fixed, and he shouted to me then to go into the next room where the other two posts stood ready. He fixed them to his apparent satisfaction, then he came downstairs and proceeded to tie a rope lashing round each post and the adjacent lower floor joist after he had wedged the joist up to level. He tested each post in turn, putting his whole weight against it.

"Jowl," he said when he had finished. "That's strong enough to hold the whole house. If you'd had the

contractors, they'd have wanted steel scaffolding inside and out, and then taken the wall down stone by stone, and for a week they would have been doing that job alone. It won't take me two minutes to do that. Let us get outside again."

As we moved to go out of the window, Dain shouted that she had made some tea, and we went into the kitchen. As we entered, Clow astonished me by removing his old felt hat, and dropping his arrogant manner. He looked almost self-conscious.

"Why, ma'am, you're making the place look very nice," he said. "It's beginning to look like a home already."

Dain had washed the tiles round about the hearth, and those nearest to the fire were dry and glowing red.

She laughed.

"It *should* look nice when we get another stove, and we've got the window mended and the walls and ceiling distempered, and our furniture in. Do have some tea."

Clow handled the mug as genteelly as though it were a vicar's tea party.

"Don't worry, ma'am. I'll soon have the whole place put right for you."

Once we were outside, however, and he had donned his hat, Clow's manner became pleasantly arrogant again.

"I won't need your help now, but I just wanted you to see how the job is done. Both of you stand clear. And don't be frightened. I've done jobs like this in the pits scores of times, with thousands of tons of rock ready to fall on you if you haven't done the thing right."

It was clear that he wanted an audience. He could not have had one more appreciative, although I was feeling a little apprehensive. I was glad that Dain was out of the kitchen. Clow had picked up a thin steel crowbar, about five feet in length. He held it poised as though it was a spear and he moved up to the wall like a hunter engaging a dangerous and formidable quarry, warily, but with perfect confidence. He prodded it lightly here and there, then, about three feet up from the ground, and a little to one side of the most prominent area of bulge, he pushed the point of the bar into a vertical gap between two of the stones, and, standing well back, levered one of the stones completely out. It fell on to the ground.

Again he raised the bar, and now he pushed it into the crumbled mortar between the two stones that the fallen one had keyed.

"This will do it," he shouted. "Watch out now!"

He pulled sideways at the bar. One of the stones shot out like an orange pip squeezed between finger and thumb, and, as he adroitly stepped back, the whole wall began to move slowly outwards. The bulge increased. Suddenly a yawning fissure appeared in its middle. There was a loud cracking and grinding sound, and the next moment, as though it had been hit by a high explosive shell, the wall came down, the stones tumbling on the ground and leaving a huge gap up to the eaves, through which were visible both the ground floor and first floor rooms which had been affected by the bulge, the joists and the roof itself supported only by the oak posts.

In that dramatic moment I had heard behind me a

feminine shriek of alarm.

"Almighty God! What's happening?"

It was Amy. She was standing near the courtyard wall, holding a bicycle. Clow, looking immensely pleased with himself, shouted something to her in Welsh; then in English.

"Keep your hair on, Amy. There's nothing happened that wasn't meant to happen."

It was clear that Amy had no respect or fear for Clow.

"Don't talk to me like that, you old pig!" she shouted. "It looked as though the whole place was tumbling down."

Clow ignored the insult. He climbed over the pile of loose stones in which the ash tree which had rooted itself in the wall was now half buried, and poked at and dislodged one stone that was hanging like a loose tooth near the eaves. On each side of the gap the wall now seemed absolutely vertical. I congratulated him. He accepted my tribute with quiet modesty.

"Oh, it was simple enough for anyone who has worked in the pits. *Jowl*. If only I had the mortar here, I'd be able to make a start building the thing up again this afternoon. It won't take me long to sort out the stones, but I may need a few new ones from the quarry. Get on with your work now. I can manage."

We were dismissed. I felt just a twinge of resentment, as joined now by Amy, we moved back to the kitchen. Who *was* Clow to give me orders? Was he the owner of Castle Druid, or was I? But I repressed my emotions. He had given me another striking proof of his technical knowledge and skill. He was undoubtedly as enthusiastic about putting the place to rights as we were ourselves, and if his motives were not yet clear, I knew that I must be very wary and not risk a quarrel with him.

There was nothing subtle or inexplicable about Amy. She had a temper. She wouldn't have been Welsh if she hadn't. But she was warm-hearted—and good-natured. She'd simply come, as she said "to give us a hand with the work". She brought the news that she'd popped into the school and found the children looking very happy with Mano and the village scholars, and that Timothy was having a grand time with Sara and Nellie. Sara had not been so happy for years. Yet before we had scarcely moved out of Clow's hearing, she said:

"He's an old pig, that man. No one here likes him, and never did, with his swank and his airs. Anyone might think he was a duke, the way he goes on."

I still liked Clow, and I let this go without comment. Amy stopped at the kitchen threshold.

"I've never been so near to Castle Druid as this. I'd be too frightened. I wouldn't go in alone for a thousand pounds. Has Clow told you about Christmas Morgan?"

"Yes," I said.

Evidently she must have thought that Clow had not done justice to the story, for she at once gave her own dramatic version of it.

"It was Clow who found him, with the rope round his neck. It was nearly dark, a cold misty day in winter. Clow had a stable lantern. He had with him a young man from the town called Patsy Johns, who used to come round taking orders for cattle medicines. He was a very nervous young man and he had never seen a dead corpse before. Clow asked him to hold the body up while he loosened the rope from his neck, and when Clow loosened it, Christmas, although he was dead, lying huddled on the floor, gave a great grunt, like a pig. Patsy let go and ran out of the house, and didn't stop running till he got to Castlebridge, and he came into the Harp and fainted. He never came round these parts again."

It must have been a grisly sight: that unfortunate man with his unkempt hair and beard, and wild eyes, which would be open in death, and probably glittering wilder than ever in the light of the stable lantern. No wonder the nervous young man had taken to his heels. Yet apparently Clow had been unmoved. To his other qualities, I thought, must be added nerves of iron.

Curiously, however, having braved the crossing of the threshold, Amy expressed an immediate desire to see the very spot where it had happened, and we walked along the flagged passage, now quite light and cheerful, with the outer wall gone and open to the air. The front door was open, too. And whatever morbid thoughts passed through Amy's mind when she looked at the staircase, the broken rail, the place on the floor where the corpse had been discovered, she seemed to enjoy the experience. Madame Tussaud knew what she was doing when she opened her Chamber of Horrors.

5

OUR FURNITURE arrived early in the afternoon, the pantechnicon drawing up at our front door. The foreman in charge told us that the van bringing our pony and trap had broken down, and might be delayed some hours.

We had swept all the cobwebs and loose plaster from the ceilings, walls and windows of the hall, and the library and drawing-room, and two of the bedrooms. The floors had been swept and scrubbed, and although there were repairs to be done in all these rooms, and the walls and paintwork were hideous, they were habitable.

I had cleaned the frame of the kitchen window, ready for re-glazing with the panes that Eddy had promised to send out with his lorry. I had pulled down the old rotten staircase. It left a huge gap in the ceiling, but that could be planked in later. I had made a makeshift door, and the red tiles on the floor, now that they were dry, looked very good.

The first piece of furniture to be carried in was the kitchen table from our Yorkshire home. Then came the kitchen stools and chairs, and the large Welsh dresser we had bought at a sale long ago, little thinking then that it would ever go into a Welsh home. It fitted perfectly against the wall opposite to the fireplace.

But the removal men were anxious to start their long return journey back to Yorkshire. We couldn't start laying linoleum and carpets until the floors were dry, and we decided to have the rest of our things put temporarily in the drawing-room. Dain had made a pot of tea for the men. We had no food to offer them. But Amy suggested that, as their way took them through Castlebridge, she should go back with them, and they'd have a meal at the Harp.

It had made us a little homesick, hearing their broad Yorkshire accents, slow and deep, mingling with Amy's quick Welsh-inflected English. They were the last link with our home county. Clow had remained aloof during the unloading operations. He hadn't offered to help, but had continued at his job of sorting out the fallen stones, never offering a word to the men as they passed him, yet giving them what I thought to be an occasional condescending glance.

Scarcely had they gone than Eddy's lorry arrived. Its principal load was the mortar for the rebuilding of the wall, and for that reason Clow directed it round to the back of the house. Far more exciting for us was the fact that on top of the mortar was a cooking-range, a bath, sink, a WC and cistern, a lavatory bowl, coils of lead, and lengths of straight galvanised piping, three complete secondhand window sashes, and the newly-cut panes. Eddy had more than kept to his word. He had even sent us two sacks of hard coal.

It was the stove that excited us most. It looked as though it had originally come from a ship's galley. It was self-contained, with a wide flat top with round movable lids, a large oven, and a side water heater with a tap. It stood on legs, and there was an L-shaped cast iron smoke pipe. It was very heavy, and Clow helped the man to lift it down from the lorry. Then he looked at it rather disdainfully.

"*Jowl*," he said. "I don't think much of this. It looks no better than the range that's in the place now. It's a new one you ought to have had for a mansion as grand as this!"

His remark nettled me. The stove was rusty, dirty, but it looked sound and efficient. It certainly wasn't going to look or perhaps behave so good as the cooking-range we'd had in our Yorkshire home, or the ones on show at the pre-war Ideal Homes Exhibition, or advertised in the magazines and newspapers of happier days, but blast it, that was our affair, not Clow's. I was discreet, however. I should need his help taking the old range out, fitting this one in. I said:

"You can't get new stoves these days, without a permit; and then we might have to wait months. This will have to do for the time being. Do you think we ought to pull out the old one before carrying this into the kitchen? It's going to be a pretty big job, isn't it? It's very heavy too."

I had taken the right line.

"*Jowl*, there's nothing to it whatever. Let's have the rest of the things off the lorry so that the driver can get away round to the quarry and load the timber. I can fix the damned thing easy enough, but I don t want to waste any time over it. I want to make a start on the wall before the dark comes."

There were only a few smouldering wood ashes in the old fireplace. I'd got them out by the time the lorry had been off-loaded. Clow came in with his crowbar. He set to on the old range energetically. There was no point in trying to save any part intact. It came out in bits, which I carried to the dump in the yard, and soon where it had been was just a deep cavity beneath the chimney flue. Eddy had taken measurements, and among the things he had sent out was a piece of sheet iron with a hole cut in it the size of the smoke pipe. This sheet fitted across the chimney breast, entirely shutting the flue except for the hole for the pipe.

While Dain swept up the old mortar and soot, I went out with Clow for the stove. Despite its great weight, I was certain that he would have carried it in by himself had he been able to get it on his back. But he was obliged to let me take one end, and it was just about as much as I could manage.

He had not made any more disparaging remarks about it. I could tell that he was very pleased with himself, the way he had got the old stove out, and he now seemed to be taking quite a proprietary interest in the new one. We moved it into position. I was helping him, but he was giving me my orders. He took hold of the pipe, and pushed one end of it up through the sheet. Then I had to heave with all my strength to tilt the stove so that the other end would fit over the flange at its back. With a click it went into position. The job was done.

I was hoping then that Clow would do what he'd said he was in such a hurry to do, get on with the building of the wall, and leave us alone. There is something peculiarly exciting in trying out a fireplace (even a cooking stove, and a second-hand one at that) for the first time. I wanted us to do it, almost ritually. I would lay it. Dain would strike the match. But Clow had already opened the grate, and thrust some of the jackdaws' nest debris into it. He struck a match, and set it alight. It started to roar at once, and then he said:

"Come on now. Let's have some of your coal on it. It doesn't seem so bad. There's plenty of draught."

I fetched a bucket of coal from the bags outside. When I returned again, I noted that Clow had removed his hat again, and was smiling genially. He took the coal from me and expertly laid pieces of it on the blazing sticks. Then he shut the doors and manipulated the dampers that diverted the fire round the oven. The fire still roared. But not quite so fiercely, proving that the oven damper was doing its job.

"It's not so bad," Clow said. "It's not so bad. Put a bucket of water in the boiler. It looks as though it will hold that and more. Get the rust off it all and give it a coat of stove enamel, and it will look quite smart. But I mustn't waste any more time with it. I've got the wall to build."

He went, doffing his hat as he passed through the doorway.

"He *is* marvellous, isn't he?" said Dain.

I was feeling vexed.

"Yes. Almost too marvellous. I wanted you to light the fire first, not him. Damn it, he behaves as though he owned the place."

"He certainly is bossy. But I don't think he can help it. I don't mind about him lighting the fire, although I would have liked to. It would have been just like our first fire at home, do you remember? Anyway, it does look a wonderful stove. It's going like billy-o. Do let's put some water in the boiler. I wonder how much Eddy has charged for it?"

The driver had handed me a letter, which I now opened. It was a statement, and I whistled when I read it. The whole consignment, mortar, cement, second-hand window sashes, bath, WC, sink piping and stove was under £15. He had charged only £1 for the stove. A new one would have cost at least £30.

Temporarily my anger against Clow evaporated. Putting up with his swank, his bossiness, was a small price to pay for the knowledge and skill and enthusiasm of such a workman, provided he didn't overdo the bossiness. With Dain to help I could have done the fitting of the stove without him. But I would have had to use a crowbar to move it an inch or two at a time. It would have taken us hours. Time was precious. There was so much to do before we could put the whole place right, and be independent of him.

I went out for a bucket of water. He was already at work on the foundations of the wall. I half filled the water tank. Dain had started to scrape the rust and dirt from the stove top and front.

"It's going to be grand!" she said. "The oven's getting warm already. It will look like new when we paint it with enamel. And fancy getting it for one pound. We are lucky, you know. It's going to be a lovely living-room, this. I'm dying to start the walls and the ceiling, and get the curtains up."

"I hope our curtains will meet with Squire Clow's approval," I said. "That should be one department he doesn't know everything about. I think I'd better get the panes in before he tells me how to do them."

"Oh, he's all right. We mustn't start disliking him."

No, I thought, we mustn't. But sooner or later I was going to have a showdown with him. I would have to make it clear who was the boss so far as our affairs were concerned.

I had brought the panes and the putty into the kitchen. I needed paint and a brush for the glazing job, and I began to look for these in a box of tools the removal men had carried in. There was a heavy cold chisel among the tools. Accidentally I dropped this on to the tiled floor close up to the stove, and, almost subconsciously, I observed that it made a hollow sound. I picked it up, and deliberately dropped it again in the same place. The sound was hollow.

"Dain," I said. "Listen to this!"

I exchanged the chisel for my hammer. I tapped lightly on the same tile, then on the next one, nearer to the hearth. The sound was still hollow, but at the hearth itself it was "dead". I worked back again, tapping tile after tile. For an area of about a square yard the sound was hollow, but elsewhere it was that of a solid floor. Under that square yard there was undoubtedly a cavity of some sort.

Dain was as excited as I was myself.

"It must be the cellars the men at the Jew's Harp were

talking about that were walled up," she said. "Isn't it thrilling. There might be treasure in them. If only we can get into them and explore them. Shall we ask Clow to take up the tiles?"

"Not on your life," I whispered. "We'll leave him out of this. And we mustn't do anything about it now. Not a word to anyone. We'll wait till we've finished with him. We'd better get a mat or something, and cover up the part that sounds hollow to muffle it. Let's do it now."

I took a quick walk outside, and made certain that Clow was still occupied with the wall. Dain fetched a mat. I put it on the place, stamped on it, and was certain it was efficient for its purpose of muffling the hollow sound. Then trying to repress my excitement, I started work on the window.

There wouldn't be treasure in the cellars of course. There was indeed no proof yet that we had located them. The cavity, and I had not the slightest doubt that there was a cavity, might be a well or just a pit. Cellars, however, were customary in country mansions, for wine if nothing else. Castle Druid was near enough to the coast for its early squires, had they been so inclined, to have been involved in contraband activities, for which secret cellars were indispensable. Why had they been sealed off, and when? Was there a gruesome reason? I must pump Clow as to what he knew or had been told about their existence. But I mustn't give him a hint of what we had already discovered.

There were three panes to be fitted. I had to do them from the outside, and the job took me nearly an hour. By that time it was late afternoon, and as the sky was

80

overcast the light was failing. Dain had lit a lamp. I could see her through the window unpacking our crockery and transferring it to the dresser. The stove door was open, and it was glowing red. A kettle was boiling on the top. Already the place was looking like home.

I had just finished giving the putty a final smoothing when I heard voices and the sound of hooves behind me. Looking round I saw the children, all of them, in our trap with our beloved Annabella between the shafts, actually galloping along the meadow from the main gate. Jane had the reins. Angus sat alongside her. Amelia had Timothy on her lap.

I tapped on the window to Dain. She joined me at the front door just as the trap drew up. The children were very excited, full of news. They'd loved being at school. They'd learned quite a lot of Welsh words, and they had been singing songs in Welsh too. Mano, the teacher was *ever* so nice. When they'd got back to the inn, there was the van, with Annabella in it. The driver was trying to get his engine to go, and Annabella was whinnying to get out, so Tom had helped to get her out, and the trap, and after Annabella had had some oats and a drink, they'd harnessed up. Darling Annabella! Wasn't it lovely having her again. She seemed to like being in Wales. She'd galloped almost all the way. Sara had sent out some more food for us all. Couldn't we all go down to the quarry and light a fire and have a picnic?

"It's much too late for that," laughed Dain, as she put her arms round Annabella's neck and hugged her. "We'll all have to be getting back soon. But we *can* have tea inside. Come along in, and see our new kitchen with our new stove."

It *was* getting like home!

6

CLOW WAS a paragon, and the more I realised it the more I saw how foolish I would be to offend or quarrel with him, no matter how he irritated me. He worked at the wall at an astonishing speed, and except at meal times he never seemed to take a rest. He refused politely to take any meals with us. He had a Thermos flask and a "bait" tin, and he ate and drank standing up where he was and looking all the time at the job where he had left off as though impatient to get on with it. I observed this out of the tail of my eye, for I knew he didn't like to be watched. It was not until he had come to the level of the window sills that he required (and commanded) my help.

The windows were for the three small rooms that adjoined the larder. We had decided that the one next to the larder should be the bathroom, the next a box-room and the last one the toilet. Clow was confident of finding the original sanitary drain leading down the meadow to a covered-in pit. When we located the pit we should have to convert it into a septic tank—a device unheard of in the days of the early squires, which automatically purifies sewage.

It was not without some argument, and the exercise

of restraint and tact on my part, that we had agreed on the ground floor arrangements. Clow had contended that in a gentleman's house the bathroom should be upstairs, not next door to the kitchen. Dain rightly argued that with young children to keep clean this would be most inconvenient, especially as all the water would have to be carried to it until we got our plumbing fixed. I nearly said to Clow that it was not a gentleman's house anyway, but I wisely refrained. To do the thing in style I said, we should have two bathrooms, one of them certainly upstairs. This seemed to mollify him.

He was a snob. And yet I sympathised with him. Undoubtedly he had the blood of the old squires in him. Undoubtedly he had a deep affection for the place, and his desire to see it restored to its one time splendour was understandable and sincere. My ownership of Castle Druid must have rankled with him too. I was an outsider, a foreigner. I wished that I could make him see that, while I had no aspirations to be known as the squire of Castle Druid, I was as anxious as he was to restore it and make it look beautiful; but that apart from wartime restrictions on materials, our spending had to be restricted. We just had to do things on the cheap.

The second-hand windows which Eddy had sent us would have cost at least six times what he had charged for them if they had been new and made to order. Clow didn't like them. They were different shapes and sizes; odd ones in fact. They would, he said, spoil the look of the wall he was building. It was true that they would. But this was the back of the mansion, I pointed out. It was the front view that counted, as he himself had said the first day we had seen it. And the windows there, like the masonry, were all right. They only needed painting.

"All right," he had conceded. "But if it was mine, I'd have the back looking as good as the front, and all the windows matching."

It would take him, he had said, about ten days to finish the wall. As he had assured us that the roof was quite safe we had moved in at the end of the first week. We had decided that for the time being, the children should continue at the village school. They would drive there and back in the trap, leaving Annabella to graze in one of the Jew's Harp fields. Mother and Sara and Amy had begged us to let Timothy stay on, but Dain's maternal instincts were too strong for this. She must have at least one child in the house.

By this time the kitchen was taking shape. We had cleaned and enamelled the stove. Dain had even polished the brass tap of the side boiler. I had covered in the gap in the ceiling left by the dismantled staircase with some of the boards that Eddy had sawn for us. We had white-washed the ceiling and distempered the walls a light pinkish grey. Unlike the main rooms of the house and the bedrooms, the kitchen windows had no shutters, and we had to have blackout curtains, but Dain had faced these with coloured gingham, and they looked light and gay from inside.

I hadn't dared yet to pump Clow about the cellars, and we had kept our discovery from the children, in case they might babble about it. Although the temptation was great, I hadn't weakened in my resolve to defer excavations until Clow had finished his work on the house. That, unless we quarrelled, would not be for some time, for there were thousands of jobs to be done. Then there were the farm buildings and cottages, all of which had to be repaired. There was the farm itself. It might be that seeing he was our nearest neighbour, and keen on farming, he would help us at least with the fences and boundary walls. There would be nothing then to bring him into the mansion. The coast would be clear.

It looked now as though our biggest problem was going to be the plumbing, the kitchen sink, the bath and toilet and hot-water system. Eddy hadn't been able to find a second-hand domestic boiler, but he had "wangled" us a new one which he had sent out on approval. It was a double-purpose stove. It would serve as a space heater, and it had front doors which could transform it into an open fire. It was finished in grey vitreous enamel, and it was expensive. But the service tank and hot water cylinder he had sent with it were both second-hand, and ridiculously cheap and we'd decided to keep it. What Eddy could not supply, however, was a plumber. His own plumber had been called up. He did not know of one in the county who could tackle the job at present.

Clow couldn't help. Plumbing, he told us with unusual modesty, was the one thing connected with building that be knew nothing about. I was relieved to find that he approved of the stove itself. Nor did he criticise our plan, arrived at after much cogitation, to install it in the library, in place of the Regency fireplace which we'd move to the John Nash room.

There were cupboards, reaching to the ceiling on

each side of the fireplace. One of these would hold the hot-water cylinder and make a perfect airing cupboard. The service tank would go on the floor above. The library which was at the north side of the house would benefit by having a continuous burning fire in it. The snag was its distance from the bathroom but if I lagged the hot water pipe with felt there would not be much loss of heat.

Could I do the plumbing myself?

I'd had a little experience of the art, but only of what might be called cold plumbing.

In our Cornish hut, I had rigged up a water supply to our ex-yacht bath and kitchen sink, using rubber hose and odd lengths of lead piping from an oil drum storage tank fed from the rain water gutter. I had contrived the necessary joints in the pipes by bringing the parts together and binding them with splints lashed with tarred cloth and fishing line. I had rigged other pipes to convey the waste water from bath and sink to a deep covered pit in the garden. It was an arrangement that would not have been approved by the sanitary authorities. Our cove had been too remote for such people to bother us, however, and the thing had worked.

Our Yorkshire home had been professionally built, and I had watched the whole process from the laying of the foundations. With a particular interest I had watched the plumbers, noting how they made their piping joints with blowlamp, white metal and flux. It had looked easy enough. I was certain that with a bit of practice I could do it.

But the installation of the toilet and bath depended on Clow finding the drain. It would run close to the foundations of the wall, and these were still covered with the debris of the demolition. Almost as essential as both these conveniences was the kitchen sink.

Dain wanted this to be fixed in front of the window which looked out on to the meadow. It was not of immediate importance to have a water supply to it, either hot or cold. I had temporarily put the service tank just outside the kitchen door, and run a double length of garden hose to it from the spring. For the kettle or side boiler, all we had to do was to dip a pan into the tank. The sink, however, had a waste pipe, and this had to be led into a drain. If we ran it to the bathroom drain (when we found it) it would mean taking up the kitchen tiles and burying the pipe beneath them, a thing we certainly did not want to do until we had found out about the cellars. It would be simpler to do what we had done in Cornwall. Dig a soakage pit a few yards away from the house, and pipe the waste into it.

I thought that I had better consult Clow before starting the job, for it would mean piercing the wall under the window for the pipe. He came into the kitchen, politely removing his hat again. I had seen that the mat was in its place over the tell-tale tiles.

To my relief he gave my proposition his unqualified approval. It would only take him a few minutes to drive a hole through the wall. But he couldn't resist telling me what I had to do—as though I didn't know! Outside of it we'd need a trap to make it easy to clear the sink pipe if it got choked. The pit needn't be more than twenty feet away from the house, and needn't be very deep if it was only for washing-up water, and it should be easy to dig, for it was old garden soil. When I'd got the trench dug, he'd come and have a look at it.

I had already made a wooden stand to hold the sink, and on one side of it a large draining-board, and on the other side a level board for holding unwashed crockery. Fortunately, the original lead waste pipe (complete with "goose" neck), although disconnected from the sink, was long enough to reach through the wall. Clow fetched his crowbar. Working first from the inside (and as an extra precaution I stood on the mat while he was doing so) he prised out one of the wall stones near to the floor. Then with the sledge he hammered the bar as far as it would go, and withdrew it. He went outside then, prised out another stone which the bar had already loosened. The hole was made and we put the pipe through.

The hole was very big, and again Clow could not resist telling me what to do. I must get some of his mortar (could I use a trowel?), break up the stones he had removed and pack them in round the pipe inside and out. He'd do it himself if I couldn't manage it, but he didn't want to waste time on it when there was the other job to do.

I could have told Clow, blast him, that not only did I know how to use a trowel, but that in our Cornish home I had built a complete fireplace of stones gathered from our beach (mixing my own mortar), with a chimney stack and a concrete hearth. The fact that the fire had smoked had nothing to do with my skill as an amateur mason. That in our Yorkshire home I had built a garden wall that was almost undistinguishable from the work of a professional. It had taken me many months, and there was one section of it that was not quite perpendicular, but only an eagle-eyed expert would have noticed it.

He made no remark about the joinery I had done for the sink.

I thanked him for his help and advice, and told him that I had a trowel in my tool box, and thought I could manage the job all right.

I decided that I would dig the pit first. Timothy decided that he would help me, using his toy spade, bucket and little wheelbarrow. I measured a distance of 20 feet from the wall and, with pegs, marked off a four-foot square from which I first removed the sods.

Clow had told us that in his father's day, there had been a flower garden extending along the whole front of the mansion with an ornamental iron fence, and a double gate for the carriage drive. Not a vestige of the fence remained, but I could tell from the first spadeful of earth I removed that he was right about this being garden soil. It was a rich dark loam, with an exciting musty smell.

It was easy to dig. As I shovelled it out, Timothy manfully started filling his wheelbarrow with it. I had explained to him that I was digging the pit to take the water from the sink pipe, and so that he should feel that his co-operation was essential and worthwhile, I asked him to tip his loads a few feet away from the hole and make a heap of them.

This amused him for a while. Then in the manner of young children he got bored. He saw in the small heap of soil he had collected the material for a new and more diverting occupation. The soil was moist but not quite moist enough. Close up to the house was a heap of old tin cans, deposited there presumably in the days of Christmas Morgan. One of them contained water. Water and soil make mud, and mud with a suitable utensil, and he had this in his toy bucket, makes mud pies.

He was clad in dungarees, with rubber shoes on his feet. He was taking no harm, and he was happy. I got on with my digging, and in one corner the pit was down to more than a couple of feet when Timothy shouted to me.

"Look, Daddy. I've found a yellow penny."

I was standing in the pit.

I saw him running towards me, looking very excited.

In one of his muddy hands he was tightly holding some object which I could not at first see. He was so excited that he stumbled at the edge of the pit. I got out and helped him to his feet. He had hung on to the object, however, and now I saw it. It was like a ha'penny in size. And it was most definitely yellow in colour. I took it from him, rubbed the mud off it, and I gasped, for as a boy not much older than Timothy, I had found such a coin on the beach of my native Yorkshire village after a rough sea. Mine had been a spade guinea, of the reign of George III, and so was this. On one side it bore a shield, shaped like a pointed spade, and the date 1794. On the other side was the head of the King.

"Where did you find it, Timothy?"

He pointed to his heap of soil.

"Over there."

I moved over and looked.

"Is it a real penny? Can I spend it?"

I hugged him.

"A penny? This is a golden penny, worth two

hundred and forty or rather two hundred and fifty of the other sort, and when you learn to count you'll know there's a difference. Are you sure you found it in the soil you brought from where I was digging? "

"It was just there," he said, pushing his spade into the mud he had made.

I tapped at the kitchen window. Dain was making a cake. But she opened the window. I showed her the coin. I kept my voice low.

"Look what Timothy has found. A guinea piece, and it must have come out of the hole I'm digging. Can you hear Clow working at the wall? We mustn't let him know about it yet. There may be some more."

"How exciting. Perhaps it's the treasure the men were talking about. I'll come out and help to look when I've got the cake in the oven. Clow's busy. I can hear him."

I handed the coin to her for safety.

"Come on," I said to Timothy. "Let's see if we can find some more."

I turned his own heap over very carefully with my spade. Then, and he willingly helped me, I did the same with the rest of the soil I had removed from the pit. We found nothing, but I thought it would be a good thing to keep the soil in a heap, let it dry and then sift it. I returned to the pit and went on digging, looking carefully at every spadeful as I lifted it out. Timothy, soon bored again, returned to his mud-pie making.

I had got down to about three feet when the character of the soil changed. It was more clayey, and mixed with stones which resisted my spade. I had to pick them out by hand. Then I struck what seemed to be either a large stone, or the living rock. If it was rock then I should not be able to dig deeper. I scraped at the stone to try and find an edge to it so that I could lever it up. I could find no edge, but what I did find was that its surface, unlike the other stones I had removed, was smooth and level. I bent down and cleared the soil away from it with my hand. It was not an ordinary stone. It was a slab of dressed slate, similar to those which formed the shelves in the larder. I gave it a tap with the edge of my spade. It sounded hollow, just like the tiles of the kitchen had done.

Excitedly I went on clearing the soil from it. I found one edge running dead straight across the pit. The other edges must be hidden under the part where I had not dug, and to find them and lever up the slab I would have to make the pit wider, starting from the top again. I got out, and to my dismay saw Clow walking round the front of the house.

"I think I left my crowbar by the window," he shouted as he drew near. "Have you seen it?"

I hadn't noticed it, but it was there. He picked it up and came towards me. I had no time to shovel the soil back to hide the slab from him.

"So you've started on the pit, eh? You should have dug the trench for the pipes first." He looked into the pit. You'll have to go deeper than that for the water to drain away. *Jowl,* what's that you've struck at the bottom? It looks like a slate slab."

I couldn't protest. He got into the pit, felt the surface of the slab with his hand, then tapped it lightly with the point of his bar.

"*Jowl*, it sounds hollow. We'll have to get this up. Give me your spade."

I felt as a child might do, compelled to watch a bullying older brother or sister opening his own Christmas parcel. There was after all a slight possibility that the slab hid treasure trove, or at least something of archaeological interest. It might be the lid, and indeed it looked like one, of a prehistoric coffin. But again I choked back my anger. I could not with dignity object to Clow doing the extra digging. I was forced to admire the speedy and efficient way he was doing it. But I was determined that when he had cleared the edges of the slab I would assert my authority and be the first to lift it up, if I could do so.

Dain had joined us. I explained to her what Clow was doing, but I signed to her to keep mum about the guinea. Timothy was quite happy with his pie-making. As each shovel of soil came out I brushed it with my foot. Clow could not have guessed what I was looking for.

It didn't take him long to get down to the level of the slab at the increased width. I was determined to take over at the right moment, and I said, firmly:

"Look, Clow, I'd like to lift it when you get it clear, if you don't mind. I'd like to see what is under it."

"Mind?" he answered, agreeably. "Of course I don't mind. That is if you can do it. It's going to be heavy. Wait now. I think I've found the other edge."

He was bent down, using his hands to remove the last remaining soil at both the sides and the ends, and suddenly he stood up.

"Why, I can see what it is. Look, there's other slabs at each end of it, just showing. I'll loosen it. Then you can lift it if you like. It's a drain, like the drain there'll be on the other side of the house for the bath and the closet. You'll have no need for your pit after all, if it's not choked up. It couldn't be better."

He put the point of his bar under the nearer long edge and levered it up an inch or two. I saw that the slab was rectangular, about four feet in length, eighteen inches in width and a couple of inches thick. I got in, alongside Clow, inserted my fingers under the raised edge and heaved it up until it was vertical, like the open lid of a hinged box. Beneath it was a cavity extending out of sight under both walls of the pit.

It was a drain, although it was big enough to merit the word culvert. It was formed of horizontal and vertical slabs similar in size and shape to the one I had raised, closely fitted together. One could have made a miniature model of it with dominoes pieces. It seemed to be perfectly clear. There was a perceptible slope in the direction of the stream.

Recovering from my first sense of disappointment, I saw what a valuable discovery it was. It would be much more efficient than my drainage pit. If we couldn't find the other drain, or it was choked, we could, if this one ran down to the far end of the house, run the bathroom and toilet pipes to it. I felt elated, especially as I had scored a mild victory over Clow in insisting that I should lift the slab. He was soon giving his orders again, however.

"Fetch a couple of buckets of water. We'll have to see if it's clear and drains away."

I fetched the water. He tipped it into the drain. It disappeared at once through the hole nearer to the stream. We emptied the second bucket, and he crouched down with his ear near to the hole, for a minute or so. Then he stood up.

"That's all right. I could hear it running away beautifully. We'd better have the slab back till you get your trench dug and your pipes laid. I'll join it up for you when you're ready so as to make a proper job of it. And now I must get on with the wall."

When he was out of sight, Dain said:

"It is exciting about the guinea. You haven't found any more, have you, Timothy? Oh dear, you are getting in a mess. Aren't your hands cold?"

It was clear that to Timothy guinea hunting was not so exciting as his mud.

"No," I answered for him. "But we've looked, and we'll keep on looking. It was probably dropped out of the pocket of one of the old squires when he was admiring the roses in the garden. But it's worth another guinea to have found the old drain. And did you notice how his Lordship allowed me to lift up the slab? I don't think though he'd have done it so politely if it had been the lid of a treasure chest, or a trap door into the cellars, where there might be treasure. I'll watch out he's not there then."

7

THE WAR situation that Christmas was grim.

If their general offensive had been slowed down by the rigours of winter and the stubborn resistance of the slowly retreating armies, it seemed that the Nazis had got a stranglehold on Russia, and were confident of making their kill in a grand final spring assault.

In North Africa, if temporarily held in his advance on Egypt, Rommel was planning an offensive which, if successful, would unite his armies with the invaders of Russia in the Middle East.

The grimmest news came from the Far East. The Japs at last had stopped pretending. They had made their attack on Pearl Harbour, crippling temporarily the American Pacific Fleet. They had attacked Shanghai, Manilla, Guam and Wake Islands. They had landed in the Philippines, in Thailand and North East Malaya. The two biggest crack battleships of the British Navy had been sunk by Jap air torpedoes. Singapore, the Dutch East Indies, Burma, Australia itself were threatened.

But to those of us who remembered the Kaiser's War, who remembered how we sang, perhaps a little cynically at first, "The Yanks are Coming, The Yanks are Coming", there was a certain comfort in the news. The Americans were with us now.

Although London seemed to be having a respite, the air-raids on British seaports had continued intermittently. There was no hope yet that the peril would lessen. Indeed if the Russians were beaten the Luftwaffe might concentrate its attacks on Britain again, and we had written to the authorities stating what accommodation we had, and hoped to have for evacuee children. We had been told our information had been filed and that our premises would be inspected, and that if satisfactory some children probably would be sent to us in due course. At present there was not an urgent demand for accommodation.

Although Dain was disappointed, I was not sorry to hear this for there was still so much to do to the house itself. Clow had finished the wall, rebuilding it the whole way up to the eaves. He had fixed the odd windows, whose appearance he had resented, into the ground floor and first-floor rooms which had suffered from the leaking roof and the bulging of the wall. Some of the floor joists of the first-floor rooms had rotted, and we'd had to replace them, and then re-plank the floors. This, as carpentry, had chiefly been my job, but we'd had to co-operate, or rather I'd had to work under his orders, where the joists rested on the walls.

We'd had many differences of opinion, but there had been no serious quarrel yet. He was, I was convinced, scrupulously honest. He kept his own time with a large old-fashioned silver watch, tied up in a chamois leather bag and carried in his waistcoat pocket. Every night when he knocked off he took out the watch, showed me the time, and made a note of it in his pocket book. Every Saturday at 12 noon he added up the hours, and I paid him, and he crossed off the total in the book.

We hadn't had a chance yet to call on him in his own home. He was a bachelor. He did all his own domestic chores, as well as running his smallholding. He had two cows, some pigs, and was rearing some calves, and he supposed we wouldn't mind if he turned these out on the Castle Druid top fields until we got stock of our own, or we began their cultivation. They would pay for what they ate, in what they dropped, and it would only be by daytime while the weather was mild. I had willingly agreed.

We had connected the kitchen sink to the drain we had discovered. Digging close to the foundations of the wall he had rebuilt, Clow had found the other drain, made like the first, of slate slabs. He had removed one of the covering slabs. We had turned the hose from the spring into it for a while and the water ran away easily.

The drain appeared to run along the back wall past the house end in the direction of the stream. We could find no outlet in the banks of the stream itself, however, nor could we locate any pit. Prodding the ground with his bar, Clow located the continuation of the drain at a point fifty yards from the house. He dug down to it, removed another top slab. We turned on the hose again at the house end (how excited Timothy had been watching and assisting in the operation), and we had seen the water rushing down at the field end.

This, Clow had suggested, would be as good a point as any to build our septic tank. He would have been happier if he had found in the drain signs of our sink water, for at this distance from the house the two drains should have joined, but it was possible they were independent all the way, and it wouldn't matter so much where the sink water went.

He had built septic tanks before. While it ought to be in brick he could do it just as well with stones from the quarry, using cement mortar to make it watertight. It consisted simply of two connected chambers, each about four feet wide and deep. The first was a settling chamber. The other was filled with coke through which the sewage slowly seeped and in the process was subjected to bacterial action and purified.

All this was in Clow's province as a mason. It involved work which strictly speaking would have been classed as unskilled labour. Fortunately he did not jib at this. But he'd let me know several times that he was doing it as a favour. He made me feel that he expected me to be at his beck and call if he actually required my help or condescended to ask my advice about anything.

I had a ruse for dealing with this tender matter of his dignity. There was, for example, the digging of the trench for the permanent water pipe from the spring to the house, definitely a labourer's job. I marked this with a line, and started to dig without telling him anything about it. He was then plastering the inside walls of the bathroom and toilet, but I knew that he was watching me through the windows, and it wasn't very long before he came out to see what I was doing.

He knew that the trench was to be for the pipe, for my marking line extended to the point in the house wall foundations where the pipe was to enter. But I feigned ignorance as to how deep the trench should be to avoid freezing in hard frosts, and I also expressed the opinion that I was going to find it a long and difficult job.

"*Jowl!*" he said, contemptuously. "It's an easy job this, if you go about it the right way. Now fetch my pick from the house, and my narrow spade. It's got to be eighteen inches deep for the frost, but it needn't be wide enough to bury a dead sheep. I'll soon have the trench dug."

He couldn't bear to watch anyone doing a job he could do quicker and better himself. But neither did he like to see anyone doing something better than he could do it. It had taxed all my diplomacy to get him to help me with the plumbing, to be indeed my plumber's mate.

I had made it clear to him that I was an amateur, that nothing would have persuaded me to tackle it if a professional had been available. My line with him was modesty, humility almost, a complete contrast to his own, concerning his own craft. I asked his opinion when confronted with any problem. But he wouldn't rise. His unvarying answer was:

"You'll have to ask a plumber that. It's not my trade."

His help was essential, however. The galvanised pipes that Eddy had sent us were mostly in lengths of sixteen feet. As they were second-hand they were tapped at each end, and you connected them together with short threaded joints. To make them tight each pipe had to be gripped with a Stilson spanner. It took two men to do this. It was a simple enough job laying the straight lengths down to the house, to the hole in the foundations which Clow had made with his bar. But the length that passed through the wall had to be just the right length to pass through, and as there wasn't such a length, I had to cut a piece with a hacksaw, and then tap the cut end.

Eddy had loaned me a "die" for doing this, also a screw-down vice for holding the pipe while it was being tapped. It was a tricky job and I wasted three lengths of pipe before I was successful. On to this, inside the house, had to be screwed what was called an elbow joint, so that the next length of pipe could rise vertically through the ceiling to where, in the bedroom above, we had located the service tank. Here it had to be connected to a ball-tap which automatically closes and opens as the water in the tank rises or falls.

It was my first real plumbing job, and I felt immensely proud of it, especially when after we had connected up the pipe at the spring end we saw, after a long and anxious period of waiting while the air in the pipe was displaced, the water gushing out of the ball-tap into the empty tank. Timothy, who followed me like a shadow when I was doing anything connected with water, was thrilled. But Clow, although I had never lost an opportunity of giving his work praise, made no comment whatever!

This had been the most straightforward and easiest part of the job. From the bottom of the tank (I had tied up the arm of the ball-tap as soon as we had tested it) I had to fit a pipe down to ground level, with a branch off from this, to the hot water storage cylinder, which we had fixed high up in the cupboard immediately below the tank. Unlike lead or copper piping, steel piping could not be bent. Branches had to be made by inserting T pieces at the joints, and the branch sections had to be carefully measured, cut and tapped at both ends.

At ground level the pipe needed another elbow joint, and then had to run through the library wall, under the staircase to the toilet, bathroom and kitchen. The hot water pipe from the cylinder was practically a duplicate of this, except that it ran from the top of the cylinder with a vertical branch extending up and over the rim of the storage tank as a safety device. Two more pipes had to run from the cylinder to the stove boiler and these, because they had to go round several bends, had to be of lead, whose ends I had to "sweat" to brass screw-in joints, the operation which had seemed so easy when I'd watched the professionals doing it, but had proved exasperatingly difficult.

I'd had to use lead pipe too for the toilet cistern connections and bathroom taps. Yet by Christmas I had done it all except the connections to the hand-basin in the bathroom, and to the kitchen sink, and I couldn't do these until Eddy had sent us more piping.

There had been a few joint leaks when we had turned the water on. These I had quickly cured with the spanner. We had lit the stove. We had fixed it in the original fireplace. Clow had cleared the jackdaws' nests from the chimney, and there was plenty of draught. Soon the water in the cylinder started to warm and within an hour there was hot water in the bathroom tap, and still Clow had made no comment on my achievement, except to say that he thought it was a pity we'd had to put in a second-hand bath. If it had been his bathroom he'd have had everything in it modern and posh.

Christmas was Christmas, however, and we were all, including Clow himself, going to have a holiday. He wasn't going to work on Christmas Day or on Boxing Day, and he was going to knock off at 4 o'clock in the afternoon of Christmas Eve. He was working then at the plastering of the bedroom above the bathroom. Promptly at four o'clock he came downstairs and knocked at the inside living-room door. The children were playing at the quarry. Dain was getting tea ready. He removed his hat as usual. He had a large cardboard box, tied up with string, which he set down on a chair. Then he produced his watch, showed me the time, and handed me his notebook.

I had the sudden unpleasant thought (mingled with a not so unpleasing thought that it might be so) that he was about to give us his notice. I had never seen him look so self-conscious. He fiddled with his hat, kept shuffling his feet. I looked at the total at the bottom of the page, took out my wallet and counted out the notes and I added an extra one. He counted them.

"*Jowl*," he said, "you've given me a pound too much."

"It's Christmas. We'd like to add that as a little present. You've done a fine job for us."

He handed the extra note back.

"I'll not take anything that's not due," he said haughtily. "If you're satisfied with what I've done, that's all right. I don't want any tips."

I apologised.

He became even more self-conscious. Suddenly he picked up the box, and put it down on the table, in front of Dain.

"Seeing it's Christmas," he said. "There's a few things in here for the little ones, and something for yourself ma'am, but you mustn't open it till tomorrow. I've had a parcel from my sister Rosie in Canada, and I've been saving up my sweet coupons too, for I don't eat sweets, and I have no little ones of my own. And I don't smoke either and I've put in a packet of Yankee cigarettes that came in the parcel. And I wish you both and the little ones too a Happy Christmas, and good luck for the New Year. And now, *Jowl*, I'll be off."

I was astounded, not so much by his speech, by his gifts, but the fact that as he turned for the door I saw tears streaming down his face.

We tried to stop him going. Dain begged him to sit down and have tea with us. We had then nothing stronger to offer.

"It is so kind of you," Dain said. "Do stay, just for once."

"We'd like you to very much," I added.

But he closed the door without another word.

"He is marvellous," Dain said then. "It's sweet of him to have thought of giving us all Christmas presents. I'm dying to see what's in the parcel, but I suppose we ought to keep it till tomorrow. Did you notice that there were tears in his eyes when he said that about him having no little ones of his own? Poor Clow. I suppose he's very lonely really, and it's awful no one liking him very much. He can't help being so proud and boastful."

I felt very warm indeed to Clow at that moment. I was glad that he hadn't given notice. His tears had moved me deeply. But I wished I hadn't offered him the extra pound note, given him the opportunity to refuse it so haughtily. I couldn't help feeling that he had scored over me again.

8

IT WAS an austerity Christmas. There were no oranges, bananas, or other imported fruit, precious few raisins, currants, candied peel for cake and pudding and mince-pie making. Sugar was strictly rationed. So were fats, and of course all types of confectionery. We didn't fare so badly, however. A farmer friend of ours in Yorkshire had sent us a turkey. Dain had managed to make a pudding which, if it contained a large proportion of black treacle, looked at least like the traditional Christmas pudding. We had no wine or spirits.

Clow's parcel had contained packets of American candy for the children, a box of chocolates for Dain, and a hundred American cigarettes for me, as well as some bars of chocolate he had bought with his own saved coupons.

There was a war-time scarcity of toys, but we had made or contrived suitable presents for all our children. To these were added others that came from friends and relations, and Albert the Post arrived with still another bag of them on Christmas morning.

We had grown very fond of Albert, whom I had first met that night in the bar-room of the Harp. He was short, wizened, untidy, much too old one would have thought for his duties of rural postman, for which he rode, or rather chiefly pushed, a tricycle as old as himself. Apart from his postman's jacket he wore no uniform.

He had corduroy trousers and a felt hat. He was tough, however, and good humoured. He was one of the company I remembered whom Clow had rebuked for their foreboding remarks about Castle Druid. He had taken a lively interest in our reclamation of the mansion. Unfortunately, he gave me the credit for what had been done and if Clow was in hearing when he was paying his compliments I would feel very uncomfortable.

Actually it surprised me how Albert did notice our improvements for he suffered from weak eyesight. He had to hold a letter within four inches of his eyes to decipher the address. It was his habit to walk straight into the kitchen, without knocking, put his bag down on any convenient place, take out the mail, and begin a scrutiny of each letter. That would be all right if we were in, for we could help him. If we were out when he called, often we had found letters for someone else, and just as often we had found that he delivered our own letters to some other farm. When we were in, Dain always made him a cup of tea or coffee, and he would sit down and gossip for anything up to half-an-hour. No farmers in the district, he had told us once, were ever in a hurry to get their letters these days. In fact he got more curses than thanks for delivering them. Mostly they were Government forms to be filled up.

This morning we saw that he made no mistake. We still had nothing alcoholic to offer him, but he had tea and cake, and would have stayed an hour if we'd encouraged him, and for once we didn't for there was so much to do.

To the children's disappointment it was not a white Christmas. The weather was mild and damp. We had whitewashed the ceiling of the library, distempered the walls and repaired and painted most of the wainscoting.

We hadn't been able to secure a conventional Christmas tree. There was plenty of holly in the wood, and one tree, with a fairly straight stem, was covered with berries. I felled it and the children with glee had helped to drag it to the house. We'd fixed it in the library in a tub filled with stones and earth. We had candles and decorations saved from pre-war Christmases, and with the stove glowing the room which, when Clow had taken us into it first, had looked so gloomy, was warm, cheerful and gay.

We could not forget the war of course, that even on this day in many parts of the world men and women and children too were being killed, or maimed or starved or tortured, that battles were being fought on land and sea, towns, villages, people's homes were being destroyed by bomb and fire. Our radio had been damaged in the removal and was still silent. There were no newspapers.

For the children the war had little reality. This was Christmas Day and they were happy, and we were happy in their happiness. And yet I believed that my own happiness was in some degree due to the fact that for this day and tomorrow, Clow would be away on holiday, that I would be free of the wearying constraint of not offending him and precipitating a row.

There was another significance to Clow's absence. It

offered a perfect opportunity for taking up those telltale kitchen tiles, and seeing what lay below. We mustn't, I thought, seeing that we might find something unpleasant, do this with the children about. We must do it late at night when they were in bed. If we found anything agreeably exciting they'd be able to see it in the morning.

We had been asked to have our Christmas dinner at the Jew's Harp. Our excuse for not accepting was the turkey. They had insisted, however, that we should go there for tea and supper. There would be another sing-song, and it was hoped that Eddy and his wife would be coming along, although the bar was going to be closed.

We set off for Castlebridge in the trap soon after three o'clock, leaving both fires banked up but with the dampers closed so that the place would be warm on our return. Annabella was in good fettle, and having eaten an extra Christmas ration of oats and carrots, and quite a number of the children's precious sweets which they offered her in a spirit of self-sacrifice, none the less admirable through being inspired by their own temporary surfeit of confectionery.

We all rode on the level. Up and down the hills Dain and I walked. We were in high spirits, looking forward to meeting our friends at the Harp. When we reached the bridge we saw that the whole village was deserted but for one figure standing outside the Harp. It was Tom, evidently on the lookout for us, and we all waved to him. He waved back, but as we drew up I could see that something was wrong. He looked very worried.

He put his hand to his mouth.

"Don't make a noise," he said in a low voice. "Mother's asleep, and we mustn't wake her up. Come on now. Quietly. A Merry Christmas to you all." (He said this almost as an afterthought.) "You get inside. I'll turn Annabella into the paddock, but don't make a noise."

Amy came out. She too was looking very worried. But she hugged and kissed the children, who were looking rather bewildered, and then hurried them inside, not into the parlour but into the deserted bar-room, whose table I saw was laid for tea. Dain went with them, leaving me to help Tom with the unharnessing. It was not until then that he began to unburden himself of his worries.

"We've had a dreadful night with Mother, Squire bach. A dreadful night. She's given us all a fright. We had a bit of a sing-song again. Eddy arrived late on with two more bottles of whisky, and maybe we all had too much to drink but you know what it is on Christmas Eve. And Mother must have taken more than any of us. She was singing at the top of her voice, and dancing. Yes, indeed, dancing, and we couldn't get her to bed till two o'clock, and she was singing for nearly an hour before she went to sleep. And then about four o'clock she woke us all up and shouted for us to come into her room. She was lying stretched out on her bed, with her hands crossed on her breast. Her eyes were shut.

"I'm dead," she said. "I'm stiff and dead. Send for Robert the undertaker. Tell him to come and measure me for my box. Hurry up now. And get the best sheets out of the bottom drawer in the chest, and lay me out."

"We thought she was dead. We thought it must be

her spirit talking for her lips didn't seem to move. Then Amy put her hand on her chest, and said her heart was beating all right. So I ran out to telephone for the doctor. Ten miles he is away, and not wanting to be dragged out of bed at that time of the morning, and Christmas morning too. It was six o'clock when he came and in a bad temper. Amy and Sara had been waiting by the bedside all that time, both of them crying. Mother was still lying with her hands across her breast, and she'd kept on muttering that she was dead. The doctor felt her pulse, and sounded her heart, then cursed us all. There's nothing wrong with her he says except that she's had too much whisky. You're a lot of damn crazy idiots getting me out of bed for this. Now leave her alone to sleep it off . . ."

"Well, she's been asleep all day, and we've had our Christmas dinner in the bar, for the parlour's just under her bedroom, and we'll be having tea in the bar too, for the pub's closed today, and we'll all have to keep quiet and not wake her."

I suggested at once that we should pack off home and not bother about tea, but Tom would have none of it.

"We've all been looking forward to having the little ones and Amy and Sara wouldn't have you go back like that. It'll be all right if we keep quiet."

Amy and Sara had put on a wonderful spread for us. There were jellies, trifle with thick cream on it. Tinned pineapple, Welsh cakes, hot from the oven with real butter on them, and other cakes galore. Confronted with so many delicious things it was not difficult to keep the children quiet.

But Timothy, with Nellie squatting on her haunches alongside him, kept on asking for Mother. And although Amy and Sara were putting on a show of happiness, there was a constraint on the party. They and Tom too couldn't completely disguise the strain of their night's vigil, and I guessed that they wouldn't want us to stay on to supper as planned. There would be no sing-song.

There were crackers alongside each plate, and when at last the children had reached their Plimsoll marks, Amy said rather pointedly,

"You'll have to take those home with you when you go, for we mustn't pull them now and wake up Mother, must we?"

And it was just at that moment that the door of the bar-room, which had been kept closed for Mother's sake, opened, and there was Mother herself, fully dressed, with her hair neatly brushed, looking as beautiful as on that evening we had first seen her, and, it seemed, in perfect health. She looked vexed, but she gave Dain and me and the children a genial greeting. Timothy had run across to her and got hold of her hand. Then, looking severely at her embarrassed daughters and son, she let herself go.

It was in Welsh, but it was easy to tell by their faces that she was saying some nasty things to them, and after she had done she spoke to us in English.

"I'm ashamed to see you all in here, and not in the best room for Christmas tea. And why didn't they wake me up and tell me that you had come?"

"Mother," Tom protested. "You were taken bad in the night, and it was a fright you gave us. We had to send for the doctor."

"Rubbish," she answered sharply. "What would I have a doctor for? I had a good night's sleep, and you should have wakened me in time for our friends coming, and not have had the table laid in this place. We'll all move in there now, for I see the little ones haven't pulled their crackers. We'll have our party in there, and we'll have Mano in to the piano, and play games and sing, and our friends must stay here the night."

Tom had already moved to her side and taken her arm:

"All right, Mother," he said. "We'll do that. Come and sit down by the fire now and have a cup of tea while Amy lights the lamp in the parlour. We're all glad you're feeling well. The children have been asking where you were, especially little Tim there. Pull a cracker with him, Mother, and I'll pull one with Amelia. I'll go and get Mano after I've given the cows their hay."

The bar was closed for Christmas, and on the whole I was glad that Eddy did not arrive with further supplies of whisky. It was a teetotal party, and the amazing old lady, if she did not dance, was the life and soul of it, for she had the advantage over the other members of her family in having slept all day.

There was to be a children's party in the village schoolroom on Boxing Day, and Dain was not against the idea that all the children, instead of going home, should spend the night at the inn; but against Mother's persuasions, I was firm about *our* not staying, although I could not disclose my very special reason for this. Dain had guessed it.

We drove home. We carried no light and the night was very dark, but by this time Annabella knew the way too well for this to trouble us. Fortunately, before setting out we had washed up. The kitchen stove had stayed in. We drew the curtains and lit our Tilley lamp.

In its light the room, which, when we had first seen it with its broken windows, and fallen plaster, and ivy branches twining up the staircase, had seemed so terrible, now looked really lovely. We had an old-fashioned fireguard with a brass rail in front of the stove. Our Welsh dresser on the opposite wall to the stove was hung with white and coloured shining crockery. Our long kitchen table had a brown linoleum top which harmonised perfectly with the brick-red tiles of the floor. The curtains gave another note of pleasing colour. Even the sink, still without its taps, looked good, for I had boxed in the under part of it to make a cupboard.

"It does look nice," Dain remarked. "But doesn't it seem quiet without the children? Listen. There's not a sound anywhere. It's almost spooky."

I did listen. There was no wind to rattle windows or shutters or set doors creaking. The silence was indeed complete, but it was broken by the sudden hooting of an owl, so loud that it might have been sitting on the roof above us.

"That," Dain said, with a shudder, "sounds even spookier."

I laughed.

"The clamorous owl, that nightly hoots and wonders at our quaint spirits," I quoted. "It does sound a bit spooky. And it's certainly quiet without the children. But isn't it nice feeling that we've got the place to ourselves? No Clow to watch us, and tell us what to do. Come on. It's our chance. We've got to see what is under the tiles." I lit one of his American cigarettes. "If he were here, he'd want to explore it first. And I'm hanged if I'm going to let him do that."

Dain laughed, too, but perhaps a little uneasily.

"But supposing there's something nasty underneath? Supposing we find the skeleton of the squire's wife or her lover? Have you forgotten what the old lady said about them disappearing mysteriously. Why should the cellars, if there are any cellars, have been walled up?"

I could not answer that, but I said:

"If the squire's wife and the gardener had disappeared under suspicious circumstances, the police would have made a thorough search of the place, and they wouldn't have failed to notice that hollow sounding patch on the floor. All old places have their stories and legends like that, as well as stories of buried treasure."

"Well," she said, as the owl hooted again, "I hope we don't find anything nasty. It would be awful to open a grave at this time of night, especially Christmas night. I wish that owl would go away."

"Graves," I said, as I removed the mat and tapped lightly on the tiles with my hammer, "are not hollow. And we're not going to find one." I was beginning to feel a little uneasy myself, and I was relieved when Dain laughed, and said:

"I was only joking. Really I am excited about it. Wouldn't it be wonderful if we found a box of guineas like the one that Timothy found? I'll put the kettle on and we'll have some tea."

Clow had left his tools in a corner of the kitchen. Among them was a small hand-pick, with a sharp point, used for making holes in roofing slates. With this I cleared the mortar along the edges of one of the tiles, and soon levered it up. Beneath it was a bed of ordinary mortar, but before digging into it I removed all the tiles within the area that had given the hollow sound, and Dain stacked these tiles by the hearth.

The job took us about twenty minutes. The kettle had boiled, and we paused to drink our tea. The owl had stopped hooting. The night was dead still again.

I started on the mortar. It was soft and crumbly. I loosened it first with the pick, then shovelled it out into a heap, making a narrow trench from one side of the patch I had cleared of tiles to the other.

This was about six inches deep. I began to deepen it, using the pick again, and now, instead of the pick penetrating the whole length of its point, there was a hard resistance about four inches down from the bottom of the trench. I cleared out some of the mortar with my bare hand. Beneath it was slate, looking exactly like that we had found in the pit outside the house, forming part of the drain.

I was bothered.

"Good heavens! We've struck a drain again. I hope it's not the drain we've connected the sink to."

"But how can it be? Didn't that run down the meadow?"

"We *thought* it did. But we never found it running into the other one."

"Well, better a drain than a grave," Dain said hopefully. "Let's go on clearing it."

I carried on, energetically, but not with the same enthusiasm as before, for working as I was close to the excavation I had already detected an odour emanating from it. It was, I was certain, the odour of stale sink water. Yet how could the drain we had found lead under the kitchen floor? It had definitely slanted down the meadow. The water we had poured into it as a test had run away quickly.

As I shovelled the mortar out I began to wish that after all I had told Clow about our discovery, that he was here to help at least with his advice. But when I had got the whole slab clear I was glad that he wasn't. The slabs of the drain were rectangular and narrow. This one was square, about three feet each way and its edges were loosely resting not on other slabs but on masonry.

I halted, and as the smell was still noticeable I lit another of Clow's cigarettes. Dain took one too. She was looking a little apprehensive.

"Shall we leave it until tomorrow?" I volunteered. "There is *certainly* something under that slab. It's not the squire's wife or her lover. I don't think it's the drain. But I'm bothered about the smell. I'm certain it is old washing-up water. It's just the smell you get when a sink pipe is blocked up and you clean it out."

I was not surprised when she answered without hesitation:

"We just can't leave it now. We must lift up the slab and see what is under it. Come on. I'll give you a help. It looks heavy enough. Do you think we can manage it without Clow?"

I laughed ironically.

"Of course we can. Especially as he's left us his crowbar. I'm glad his lordship is *not* here. He'd have just made us watch him lift the thing, and he'd have been the first to look."

I took the crowbar, which he had left with his other tools. I inserted its chisel point centrally at one edge of the slab, and gently began to prise. It moved slightly upwards, and I called to Dain to bring the poker and insert it alongside the crowbar, and hold on until I got a better purchase with the bar. She did this, and the bar now sank down several inches. I prised again. The slab began to rise like the lid of a box, and Dain, who wasn't expecting this, let go of the poker. It slid down into the gap between the round edge of the slab and the masonry on which it had been resting, out of sight, and then below we heard a *splash*.

As my ears registered that rather disconcerting sound, my nose registered a more concentrated odour coming up through the gap. I was aware of an upward draught of air too. I asked Dain to hang on to the crowbar while I got my hands under the slab. I got a good purchase, gave a heave, and the slab came up into a vertical position. I pushed it over on to the heap of mortar.

The lid was off. There was a gap in our kitchen floor three feet square. Beneath it was impenetrable darkness.

In spite of the smell and my anxiety as to what it might signify, we were both excited now. Taking a chance with the blackout regulations, we had opened the kitchen doors, and partly drawn the curtains of the window. Whatever lay below, the air could not be dangerously foul for there was still a strong draught blowing out of the hole. It was obvious that the cellar or whatever it was had some other outlet either inside or outside the house. I decided to be on the safe side and make a test before we began to explore.

I lit a stable lantern, tied a line to its handle, and lowered it slowly down until the line slackened, showing that it had struck bottom, at a depth of about ten feet. Again there was a splash, but I could tell by the feel of the line that the lamp was not afloat. There could not be more than an inch or two of water. I lay flat on the kitchen floor and peered down. The lantern dazzled me. All that I could see was that on the side nearest to the kitchen hearth a stone wall fell vertically, and that on the opposite side there was an arch which seemed to extend under the kitchen floor. The slab had been placed at its highest point.

Clow had left his ladders in the passage. I fetched a twelve-foot one, and lowered it down this hole.

"The lantern is burning all right," I said. "If the air was foul it would go out, but we'll give it a few more minutes. Are you game for going down then?"

"Of course! I'm dying to explore it. But don't you think it would be a good idea to put our gas masks on first?"

I had thought of that, but having listened to an A.R.P. lecture on the use of those hideous and uncomfortable devices with which we had all been equipped at the outbreak of the war, I knew that they would have been of no value against any vapours that we might encounter. The lantern was evidence that there was plenty of oxygen. Although unpleasant, stale dish water should not be poisonous, and already the smell was not so strong as when I had first lifted the slab.

"No," I said. "All we need is our gumboots, and another cigarette each. I'm going first of course. But I'll wait for you at the foot of the ladder."

We had changed into overalls before taking up the tiles. We put on our gumboots, then carrying an electric torch I stepped on to the ladder, and began the descent. From the bottom rung I stepped on to a hard floor that had not more than two inches of water on it, and deliberately I did not look round me until Dain was down and by my side. Then I lifted up the stable lantern, and with that and the torch we looked about us.

It *was* a cellar. It was arched under the whole width of the kitchen floor above, with its highest walls at the hearth side and the side opposite. In this opposite side, which was nearer the main building, was another smaller archway, the opening of a passage, and it was through this there came a definite current of untainted air.

But for the moment it was the wall which was under the kitchen window (and the sink) that held my interest, that and the water on the floor, which undoubtedly was water from our sink. There wasn't so much of this after all. In fact some of the floor was dry. It was, however, dripping down the wall face. Clearly it was coming from the drain we had opened, and optimistically led the waste pipe into. This somewhere in its course was blocked and at some point broken, allowing the dammed waste to seep through the soil and through the cellar wall.

We could, by digging up the drain, find where it was blocked and clear it. Chloride of lime would soon neutralise the water that had seeped into the cellar, and it would soon dry up. But I trembled to think what would have happened if we hadn't taken up the tiles and the slab. In six months the cellar would have been at least half full.

"What a bit of luck we've found it in time!" said Dain. "But there doesn't seem to be anything else in the cellar, except the water."

"We haven't seen it all yet. Look! That passage must lead somewhere. Come on. There's air blowing through it. Perhaps this was a smuggler's cellar, and we're going to find an entrance outside the house, perhaps in the wood."

"How exciting. Come on."

The entrance to the passage seemed to be immediately below the doorway from the kitchen into the flagged passage that joined the kitchen to the mansion. Its arch was much lower than the main cellar, and it was only four feet in width. I flashed the torch into it. At the far end, at a distance which I judged to be the same as the passage above, was a blank wall. Its floor too was flagged and, although damp, was free of sink water. We moved along it, Dain holding my hand, our footsteps making an eerie echo. We could still feel the draught of good air.

The walls were solid on either side of us, straight, and well-built of even slate blocks. Just short of the end wall, and under what I guessed would be the rise of the staircase in the hall above, there was another archway to the right, another but shorter passage. It ended in another blank wall, but both to the left and right were arches. That on the left was wide, and there was a recess about six feet in from the passage forming another cellar. On the floor close to the walls were mounds of brown mould, and there were rows of small cavities, some with rotten ends of wood still projecting from them. It was clear that there had been wooden racks here for holding wine bottles. The mould on the floor was the debris of the racks. There was no wine, however. Not even a broken bottle to give us a clue as to the date the cellar had last been used.

I was disappointed.

"Whoever closed up the cellars must have taken pains not to leave anything behind," I said as I brushed my foot through one of the mounds. "I was hoping that at least we'd find a keg of brandy, or an old pistol, or something like that. They might have done it with a vacuum cleaner, if such things had been invented then."

"Well, we haven't finished yet," Dain said hopefully. "There's still one more passage to explore. And anyway we haven't found anything nasty."

I turned the beam of the torch into the narrow archway on the right through which the draught was blowing. It was about eight feet along, and apparently led under the John Nash room, which because of the dangerous state of the ceiling, we had locked up lest the children should venture into it.

Again Dain took my hand as we walked along the

passage. We entered another cellar, arched from left to right, a little bigger than the one under the kitchen, and differing from it in one other important respect. On the right-hand wall there was a cavity up which there rose a flight of spiral stone steps like those of a lighthouse.

The cellar was empty but for the brown mould of decayed bottle racks. My theory that the draught of air came from a passage out of the house was dispelled by the sight of the staircase. We had merely found the old wine cellars of the mansion, and this must be the last, or rather the first of them, for the staircase obviously had been the way in. Yet where was the entrance? The current of air was coming down the stairway cavity.

We mounted the steps, shining the torch upwards.

They ended above the cellar roof in a sort of landing, with another archway which was filled in with bricks. Some of the bricks had crumbled however, and there was a hole through the wall through which there blew a steady stream of air. I shone the light into the hole and saw woodwork, panelling partly rotted, so that the air was coming through it, and I knew where we were.

"It's the Nash room," I said. "The wainscoting. This must have been the entrance to the cellars, either by a proper door, or a sliding panel. It might have been for smuggling, of course. The cellars might have belonged to an older house, before Nash built the present place. Anyway, there's nothing here. No treasure, no corpses, nothing."

"How disappointing! But I'm not sorry about the corpses!"

"Well, they *might* have left something, if only some

writing on the wall. Initials, a date or something like that. Think what the Egyptians or the Assyrians would have done, not to mention the prehistoric cave-dwellers!"

I shone the light round the walls, still hoping that we would see something. And then for the first time we saw at the top of the staircase, a small niche in the wall, and in the niche an object.

"Look!" I cried. "Look at *that*!"

Dain was nearer to it than I was. She picked it up, held it in the beam of the torch. It was a candlestick, about nine inches high, slender, beautifully shaped. It was covered with dust, tarnished. I felt the weight of it. It was heavy, and I thought it must be pewter. But when I rubbed the stem with my thumb, I saw a whitish gleam.

"Gosh! I think it's silver. I'm almost certain. If it is it will have a hallmark on it with the initials of the maker and perhaps a date when it was made. I'll swear it's not later than Queen Anne."

"It's lovely, lovely. Look, there's even some tallow in the holder, and a bit of wick. It must have burnt out, and that's why it wasn't noticed when they shut up the cellars. I wonder how long ago it was. I am excited about it. Aren't we lucky?"

"We're luckier still, not having Clow with us," I said, "that we've done this on our own. He wouldn't have bagged it, but he'd have been the first to find it." I began to feel a little uneasy. "I wonder what he'll say when he learns we've found the cellars. I think I'll have to tell him that we were worried about the smell, and that's why we removed the tiles. We mustn't replace them until we've dried out all the sink water, and we mustn't use the sink until we've cleared the drain. Come on, let's get back to the kitchen now. We'll put some disinfectant in the water, then put the slab back temporarily, and we can explore the whole place again in the morning."

"Yes. But we must clean the candlestick before we go to bed. Won't the children be excited when they see it! What a happy Christmas it has been!"

9

THERE WAS an air raid on Merseyside early in the New Year. A few days later the first three of our evacuee children arrived. They were Liverpool Protestant Irish, their name O'Riley. There was Mary aged eight, Kathleen five, and Ellen three. Their father was a tugman. Their house had been destroyed by blast. There were four older children, and the mother was in a maternity home having still another when the raid had happened. None of the family had been hurt.

Somewhat to Dain's disappointment, I thought, they were not problem children. They were all pretty, with black hair and grey eyes, and clear healthy complexions. They spoke with a Liverpool twang but there was more Irish than Lancashire in it. They were clean, and tolerably well behaved, with no more "divil" in them than would be found in most children of their age, including our own.

The only trouble we had was that Mary considered herself to be in charge of her sisters, with all the duties and responsibilities and authority of their mother, and at first she obstinately refused to delegate her trust to anyone else. She wouldn't let them out of her sight. She insisted that they should all sleep in the same bed, that she should wash them, dress them, make them behave at table.

Kathleen and Ellen were too young for school. Mary was not against going to school in the trap with our children, but she wasn't going to do this and leave Kathleen and Ellen behind, although Timothy had taken to them from the start, and had offered them the use of all his playthings. Mary too objected to dungarees, and playing with soil and mud. Her ideal was for her sisters and herself to be dressed as for Sunday school: hair tidy, faces and hands clean, shoes polished.

She was taking on too much for a child of eight. But Dain, wisely, didn't rush things. Gradually, she won Mary's confidence, and above everything her love. Yet it was Jane who was more practically responsible for weaning Mary from her sisters. On Saturdays and Sundays, when there was no school, Jane would saddle Annabella, and practise steeplechasing in the meadow. She had made several jumps with thin tree branches. Mary would watch her fascinated, and, after much wheedling, Jane persuaded her to mount Annabella and have a first gentle ride.

It was the thin end of the wedge. Mary had already taken a great liking to Jane, and here was a new bond of interest. Kathleen and Ellen were millstones round her neck. She found that they were safe and happy either with Dain or with the other children playing at the quarry. She gave up the fight, even to the extent of seeing them in dungarees, and making mud pies, and not complaining. Soon she was going to school in the trap, sharing a bedroom with Jane instead of a bed with her sisters, and they in turn were more tranquil under a single authority.

The O'Rileys merged, becoming one with our own family. They did not lose their individuality in the process. They did not lose their brogue. Indeed, both Jane and Angus acquired some of it, and as they were all picking up Welsh words and phrases and inflections at school it would not have been easy to maintain a strictly correct standard of speech. Not that this bothered us. The main thing was good manners.

There were still many empty bedrooms. It was Dain's ambition to have them all in use, to fill the place with evacuee children. The Government billeting allowance for each child was only eight shillings and sixpence a week, however, not enough to cover the bare cost of their food. In Yorkshire we had grown all our vegetables with plenty of fruit in season. Our poultry had given us eggs all the year round.

It had not been practical to have our poultry sent to us. We'd have to buy some day-old chicks and rear another flock, but it would be next winter before they would produce eggs. We had no garden here until we made one and it would be late spring before we'd get even lettuces. If Dain achieved her ambition it was going to be too big a strain on our finances I felt. Besides, it would mean far too much work for her unless we got some domestic help.

We came to the reluctant decision that if we were to have any more Government evacuees, we'd have to have some private paying ones too in order to even things out. There must be some parents obliged by their jobs to stay in towns, who'd be glad to let their children come, and pay a reasonable sum for their keep. We advertised, and at the same time advertised for someone with experience of young children, to help run the place as an evacuee hostel and possibly a nursery school.

We were successful. Our first paying evacuee, Makubwa, was the five-year-old son of an African negro chief whose territory had been overrun by the Italians. The chief, who'd had a European education, held a well-paid post in the Colonial Office in London. His wife had been killed by a machine-gun bullet when their escaping column had been attacked by low-flying aircraft.

Makubwa spoke good English. Although Mary seemed a bit sniffy about his colour at first (I think it was because no matter how he scrubbed his hands they never *looked* clean), the other children took to him at once, and soon he had overcome even Mary's resentment, for he had a jolly, good-natured disposition, a strong sense of humour, and an irresistible smile.

The twins, David and Jonathan, were four and a half. They came from Coventry, where their father, an unorthodox Jew, was manager of an engineering works.

His wife had had a nervous breakdown after the Coventry raid, and was in a nursing home. He brought the children himself in a large Daimler. In spite of his air of opulence, he seemed a very decent chap, devoted to his wife and children, pathetically concerned that they were going to be happy and well looked after.

The sight of the other children must have given him some assurance that it would be so. True that he looked a little dubiously at Makubwa, but he was quick to tell us that he had no racial prejudices. He approved of the house. He was pleased that we had got cellars. We ought to fix bunks in them so that if there were any raids there'd be no danger. But the main thing, he said, was that the children should have plenty to eat. He'd be sending parcels every week, and we must let him know if we were short of anything. He knew a thing or two about the Black Market!

It was clear that the twins had been brought up indulgently. They had black curly hair, dark, placid, almond-shaped eyes, pale skins, but they were podgy, lethargic. They needed more exercise, and a judicious diet. There was nothing disagreeable about them, however. All the children liked them. Mary was particularly impressed, and wistfully admired their smart suits with collars and ties, and shining shoes, which for most occasions would have to be replaced with the garments she herself still wore reluctantly, dungarees and rubbers.

Then came Christine. Her age was four. She had golden hair, the face of a cherub, and, it seemed the heart and mind of a fiend. True that we were warned by her grandparents with whom she had been living, that she was a "difficult" child. Her father (their son) was serving overseas. Her mother had fallen in love and run away with another man. The grandparents lived in a Sussex town which so far had escaped any serious bombing. "Grannie" (we guessed that she was a rather selfish sort of person) was in poor health, however, and the strain of looking after Christine had got too much for her. They'd had two nannies, but neither of them had stayed more than a week. They had tried a nursery school, but the teacher who ran it must have soon decided that Christine would have been beyond the help of Dr Montessori herself.

A psychiatrist had diagnosed that the cause of Christine's behaviour was her broken home, her lost sense of security, that what she needed above everything was maternal love, the companionship of other young children, in a family rather than in a school. That was why our advertisement had appealed to the harassed grandparents, but I privately suspected that what had appealed most to them about Castle Druid was its geographical remoteness from their Sussex home.

Christine made a scene at tea-time on the evening of her arrival. She couldn't stand the sight of Makubwa, who was sitting opposite to her.

"He's horrible, horrible. He's got a black horrible face."

Makubwa was too good-natured to show resentment. He laughed and grimaced, which made the other children laugh, but made Christine scream. She wouldn't eat anything at all. She didn't want a bath. She didn't want to go to bed, and I had to carry her (firmly but gently, for I was very sorry for her) upstairs, kicking and screaming.

Dain had decided to put her in the same room as Ellen and Kathleen, with a cot of her own of course. She wouldn't undress. When Dain tried hugging and petting her, she fought like a wild animal and even tried to bite. But Dain got her undressed at last and into her nightie and into bed, and again tried to comfort her, and Kathleen, who was very distressed, got out of bed and offered her favourite doll, which Christine promptly rejected.

Not surprisingly she wet her bed that night. In the morning she was calmer. The elder children, including Makubwa, had gone off to school. There were only Timothy, the twins, the two O'Rileys. The twins were still a bit shy, but Timothy and Kathleen both made friendly advances to her, without getting any response beyond a scowl. She was hungry, however, and put away a good breakfast, asking for more jam. Her face puckered when Dain told her that there wasn't any, that jam was rationed, and everyone had to have just their share, but she didn't cry.

"My grandpa gives me plenty of jam, and plenty of sweets and chocolates. Just as many as I want. If I get any I won't give them to anyone. I'll eat them all myself!"

We hadn't got any help yet for the house or children. Temporarily we were using the library, with its continuously burning boiler stove, as a playroom, and after breakfast Christine raised no objection to going there with the other children. I was giving Dain a hand with the washing up.

"She is a little beggar, isn't she?" said Dain. "But I

think she'll soon settle down. We've got to be very patient with her. I'm sure that the psychiatrist was right. What she needs is love and security. I'm sure it's not her fault that she behaves like she does. She's got a perfectly sweet face. We've just got to make her happy. I'm sure that it would be all wrong to spank her for her rudeness and naughtiness."

Remembering my own childhood, and particularly the village school I attended, where you had your ears boxed, or your knuckles rapped with a ruler if you got a sum wrong or even if you dropped your slate pencil on the floor, I was against physical punishment; but I did believe, with Bernard Shaw, that if a child did something particularly wicked, and made you really angry, it was a good thing for the child and yourself to give it a slap. You had to be angry and you had to be just. You had to see the child's point of view. But it was just as important that the child should see yours.

We had just finished the washing up (I was itching to be up on the fields, where Clow was helping me repair the boundary fences) when there were shrieks from the library. We met the twins halfway along the passage, both of them yelling. Both were incoherent. Dain put her arms round them, and we took them (obviously against their inclination) back to the library.

Christine was sitting on the floor in front of the fire, playing with some toy bricks. Timothy, Kathleen and Ellen were together in a far corner of the room, Kathleen clutching her doll, all of them looking bothered. Christine, however, for the first time since she had arrived, looked perfectly happy. She even smiled sweetly at Dain. The twins now became coherent.

"She pulled my hair. She pinched me," cried David.

"She pinched me too," Jonathan cried.

Christine looked indignant.

"I didn't. I didn't. They took my bricks. I just pushed them."

It was obvious that she was lying, that the twins had been playing with the bricks, and that she had taken possession of them, pinching the twins and pulling their hair when they had protested. Timothy and Kathleen looked ready to give evidence in support of this, but they both knew that we had a rule against telling tales. Justice had to be done, however.

Dain told Christine gently but firmly to stand up. She obeyed, looking a bit scared, but still trying to maintain an air of innocence.

"You're telling a story, Christine. The bricks and all the other toys are for everyone to play with, and I'm sure that you weren't playing with the bricks first. You took them from David and Jonathan. If you hurt them you'll get hurt yourself. We've all got to be friends in this place. David and Jonathan must have the bricks now, and if you can't find anything else to play with you'd better come with me into the kitchen."

Christine looked relieved, and almost repentant.

I said nothing myself. The twins hadn't been badly hurt, for they had stopped crying, and I thought that it would have been bad policy to have made Christine tell them she was sorry. What they ought to have done I felt, was hit her back. It was not my business anyway. I was sure that Dain could manage it. Temporarily at least, peace descended on the nursery. I set off to do my job in the field.

There could be no doubt that what Christine needed above everything was affection. You couldn't force this upon her. But it was there, when she would take it, in both of us, and in all the children save Mary, who detested her. Perhaps there was some jealousy in this, for Jane did her best to persuade Christine to ride Annabella, which of course would have meant Mary standing aside.

Christine wouldn't ride. Amelia, who really liked her with all her faults, tried to interest her in her own pet hobby of natural history. It wasn't the most suitable time of the year for this. There were no wild flowers yet, nor many birds, no butterflies, frogs or tadpoles. The trout in the stream were hiding under the stones and the water was too cold for paddling. Christine was not interested. Her chief delight was teasing, and, if they had the misfortune to be caught alone, chivying the twins, despite that they did their best to be friends with her, even, we suspected, to buying her off with their sweet rations.

She didn't tease or bully Timothy, nor openly Kathleen or Ellen, but she rejected all their attempts at friendship. She was getting used to the sight of Makubwa. She would never speak to him, however, and although Dain would give her a hug, especially at bedtime, she made no response.

There was nothing wrong with her physically. As well as being pretty, she had a lean, lithe body and could run like a hare. She had a good appetite. But she bit her nails. She continued to wet her bed. She was intelligent, but she was also cunning. She was greedy and she was dishonest. The larder was raided. A pot of strawberry jam had been more than sampled, and a precious jelly square stolen. We couldn't pin it on Christine, but the fact that, when challenged, she said she saw Makubwa near the larder door strengthened our suspicions that she was the culprit.

We were both sorry for her. What saddened Dain was her apparent failure to win Christine's love and confidence. All the other children would fly to Dain if they were hurt or in trouble. Christine just yelled or sulked. The grandparents sent her a large and expensive doll. Even our own children had never possessed anything like it. Christine took it to bed with her. In the morning, to the horror of Kathleen and Ellen, she had given the doll a beating up, pulled off its hair (it was real hair too, golden and curly like her own), twisted its legs and arms till they were nearly broken, and then thrown it on the floor.

It was her own doll. She didn't, as she might have done if she had been actuated by pure spite, blame Kathleen or Ellen for having ill-treated it. It was hard then to tell what action to take beyond telling her that she had done something very silly, that the doll would have to be sent to a doll's hospital to be treated, and that she couldn't have it again unless she promised to look after it properly.

She didn't get away with everything. She got a slap or two from Dain for petty misbehaviour, and she did recognise that Dain was boss. I fancied that I was neutral in her regard. I seemed safe, but she didn't take any chances.

And then a remarkable thing happened. It was early on a Saturday afternoon, and Christine by then had been with us about ten days. The weather was dry and fairly mild. Jane, taking Makubwa and Angus with her, had gone off with Annabella to a blacksmith's shop in the district, to have her re-shod. Mary had been slightly put out by this, and hadn't seemed at all keen at the prospect of playing with her sisters and the twins, Timothy and Christine in the quarry. They had gone there, however. Dain and Amelia, who was helping Dain in the house, would join them later.

I was in the wood below the quarry, cutting some posts for the fences. I could hear the children playing, and for some time all seemed to be going well, and when I did hear the sound of quarrelling I was not seriously perturbed. Probably, I thought, Christine was chivying the twins again, but Mary was there, big enough to interfere if she really hurt them. They were too far away for me to have recognised individual voices, even the most familiar one of Timothy's.

I went on with my job. The sound of quarrelling continued for a while, and then there was relative silence. I was near the stream, with thick undergrowth close about me, but some yards away was a rough path leading downstream. Suddenly I heard hurried footsteps along the path from the direction of the quarry. I saw Christine running fast, and a few yards behind her, Mary, obviously in pursuit.

I kept still and quiet, as though I had been bird-watching. The faces of both children were flushed.

Christine was smiling confidently, her eyes sparkling, and I thought that I had never seen her look so pretty. She was like a Shirley Temple. Mary, however, had her mouth. tightly closed, and her expression was one of grim determination.

If it was a race (and something told me it was more than that), Mary hadn't a hope. She was stronger than Christine, but her legs were shorter, she was more sturdily built. And Christine must have known that she had the advantage for just as she was opposite to me, she turned her head, contemptuously, put out her tongue at Mary.

Pride cometh before a fall! At that very moment Christine tripped, and fell. Mary gave a spurt. Before Christine had got to her knees, she leapt on her, and pinned her by the arms.

"You little b—— " I was astonished to hear her say. "I've got you now."

Christine gave a coward's shriek.

"Let go—let go! I'll *tell*. Let go!"

She struggled, but Mary had her collared. She pulled her to her feet, then, very expertly, bent her over, with her left arm over her shoulder, and proceeded to smack her backside.

"You little b——. I'll learn you to pinch Ellen!" she muttered between smacks. "You mucky little b——. That'll learn you not to wet your bed. That's one for pinching David. That's one for stealing jam and blaming Macky. That's one for pulling your doll to bits. *You* pinch Ellen again . . ."

I remained still, and hidden. I felt that I was

watching an act of primitive justice, in which I had no call to interfere so long as Mary's smacks were directed in the traditional fashion. She was probably only doing what her own mother had done to her on many a justified occasion. Although I swore myself, I did not approve of the children swearing. I had never heard Mary swear before, but again I felt that she was privileged.

Christine screamed, and went on screaming. I didn't count the number of smacks, but I had no doubt that every one of them was deserved, and certainly they did her no physical damage, for as soon as Mary let go, she bounded off along the path like a hare released from a trap, and, I noted, in the direction of the house. Mary rubbed her hands together, and with a look of supreme satisfaction on her face, slowly walked back towards the quarry.

I did not witness the final scene of this little drama, but later in the afternoon, when I went up to the house, I met Christine and Amelia, walking hand in hand back towards the quarry. They both seemed very happy, and Christine even gave me a sweet smile. I met Dain just coming out of the house, also looking very happy.

"I say," she said. "A miracle has happened. Christine came running into the kitchen, sobbing her heart out. She flung herself into my arms, and actually allowed herself to be petted and kissed and she even called me Mummy. Poor kid. She wouldn't say what had happened to her. I think she must have had a fright of some sort. Anyway, she just clung to me, and somehow or other she seemed quite different. She's all right now and she's gone off quite happily with Amelia to play with the others. I wonder what could have happened to her?"

I could have told Dain what had happened, but in the best interest of all parties, I thought I would say nothing. I couldn't blame Christine for not making a clean breast of the whole affair. She had her dignity to consider. Certainly I would not tell tales on Mary. A miracle *had* happened. It was a fact that from that day on the character of Christine changed. She stopped wetting her bed. She stopped chivying the twins. She began to laugh at Makubwa's jokes. She "took" to her mended doll. Her heart completely melted towards Dain. She was cool with Mary but almost ostentatiously affectionate towards Kathleen and Ellen, which was as much as showing that she bore Mary no deep resentment.

She didn't become an angel of course. There was still plenty of normal mischief in her. But she merged, became still another member of our family. Which was as well for the following week no less than five evacuees arrived, all from the East End of London. Fortunately, in the same week, as a result of our advertisement, came "Porgy".

Her real name was Miss Angela Porson. Her father had been a farm labourer in Norfolk, and she was one of a family of five daughters and seven sons. At the age of fourteen she had gone first as kitchen maid to the local "big house". The eldest son of the house was in the diplomatic service and soon she had been promoted to nurse-help to his young family, and in this capacity and later as nanny she had travelled to, and lived in, many parts of the world, including Egypt, India, China, the West Indies, even the Falkland Islands.

She was fortyish, plump and jolly. She loved

children, and the children, including the reformed Christine, loved her. She had a passion for work. She didn't mind what she turned her hand to: housework, cooking, making or mending clothes. She liked gardening, and was soon urging us to get on with ours. She was as enthusiastic as we were ourselves about our plans for the farm. She could milk, knew how to make butter and cheese.

She was a treasure. Her only defect was her inability to put her aitches in the right place in her speech, which itself was a curious mixture of her native Essex dialect and public school English. This did not worry us until at a later period we discovered that the habit was insidiously contagious not only with the children, but with adults. I was horrified one day to hear myself say to one of the London children whose name was Harry:

" 'arry, 'ave you seen H'amelia h'anywhere?"

10

I COULD not pretend that the invasion of our new home with other people's children was an undiluted joy for me.. There was a satisfaction in the fact that we were giving them a life safer, and in many ways happier, than they would be having in their own homes during the war. I liked them all, but blood is thicker than water, and I could not feel towards any of them the same affection that I had towards my own.

Yet it would not have been fair to the evacuee children to have let them be aware of this. One's affections had to be strictly rationed and inevitably diluted, which was probably a good thing for the children themselves. An excess of love can do almost as much harm as a miserly measure of it.

I could not pretend that I liked the augmented volume of noise that was made by our enlarged family at meals, at play, and often in the night—for two of the London evacuees were year-old babies, and they'd yell for attention at almost any hour, waking up the other children as well as ourselves. I disliked the sight of children sitting on chamber pots, and I felt that this, and other rituals connected with babyhood, should be performed in privacy. Porgy apparently thought that any time and place would do, even mealtimes in the kitchen, and I lacked the courage to protest.

Far more than this, I was bothered by the increasing strain on our finances. The London evacuees were all eight shillings and sixpence a week ones. We acquired two more private payers, but in the same week came two more official ones from Southampton. We had to pay Porgy five pounds a week, although I think she would have worked for nothing rather than leave us. There was still a great deal to do to the house and farm buildings, and there was the farm itself. The fields had to be ploughed and tilled and sown, and we should need many tons of lime and artificial fertilisers. On top of this we should have to buy stock.

And there was Clow. We could not afford to go on employing him much longer. Certainly he was cheap at three and sixpence an hour. He did the work of at least two ordinary men. He came at eight and never knocked off till five. His average wage was over eight pounds a week. At present I was earning nothing.

I just could not go on like this, but I no longer looked forward with pleasure to parting with him. Indeed, I dreaded it. I didn't see how I could carry on without him. He continued to irritate me with his swank and his arrogance. Yet, since Christmas, there had been a softening in his manner. I had the feeling that he liked us, and that apart from everything else it would distress him deeply if I told him he must finish. Probably he would cry again, as he had done when he had given us the Christmas parcel.

His liking for us did not extend to the evacuees. His

ambition was to see Castle Druid restored to its once-time glory, and, he said, we'd never do that, inside or out, while the place swarmed with children. A few, like our own, were all right. They were well-behaved, nicely-spoken, and anyone could see they had quality in them. Christine wasn't so bad, although she was a saucy little devil. He didn't mind the twins and the darkie boy. But the O'Rileys and the London kids! There was only one thing to be said of them—they were working-class and common. He knew it was right that they should be kept away from the air raids, but he hoped that when the war was over they'd all go back where they belonged, and we'd have the place to ourselves.

Although I was far from being in agreement with all this, I did see Clow's point of view. It was the squire blood in him, and he couldn't help it. Although he didn't say anything, I knew that it had vexed him to see first the library and then the drawing-room handed over to the children. The drawing-room, which in his imagination he saw richly carpeted and elegantly furnished, was the inevitable choice for a nursery school room.

The mother of one of our non-official evacuees (her name was Parkinson, and we called her Parkey) was an ex-schoolteacher whose husband was with the Royal Air Force in the Far East. She had enough to live on, and she offered to join us in our venture in return for board and lodgings for herself and her child. For the time being, the elder children would continue to go to the village school, where they were all happy and doing well.

It was not, however, as a concession to Clow's feelings that we decided to mend the collapsed ceiling of the John Nash room, put in the lovely fireplace from the library, mend the wainscoting, paint the cupboards, and make it as beautiful as its unique shape merited. We wanted one room which, except on special occasions, would be reserved for adults, into which we could put our best furniture, carpet and rugs, have our books, and in which too I could—if I ever had the time or the necessary power of concentration—pursue again my profession of writing.

Clow was delighted when I told him of our decision, especially so when I said that the room would be for adult use. He hadn't seemed to be offended when, on his return to work after Christmas, we had told him about the cellars, yet he was not very gracious about it. Whatever other virtues he had inherited from his aristocratic ancestors, sportsmanship was not one of them. He had indeed belittled our discovery.

"*Jowl*," he said. "Everyone knew there were cellars under Castle Druid. I could have found them long ago if I'd looked for them, and had been in my rights lifting up the tiles. They'll be no use to you unless the Germans come. I don't suppose you'll want to use them for keeping wine!"

He hadn't been quite so crushing about the candlestick. We had cleaned and polished it, and found the hallmark which definitely dated it to the time of Queen Anne.

"That's pretty," he said, "real pretty. But it's a pity you didn't find the pair of them, to go one each side of the mantelshelf. Still, it's pretty."

I had made a permanent wood frame and trap door

to replace the removed tiles and slab of the kitchen entrance to the cellars. I had mopped up the sink water, and killed the smell of it with chloride of lime. We had found that the drain was blocked about fifteen feet down from where we had led the sink water in it. When it was clear a test proved that it did join the other drain that led to our septic tank, and we had no further trouble with it.

Clow had made no comment when I had walked through the cellars with him, not even when I had showed him the niche where we had found the candlestick. He had pushed his crowbar through the brick wall at the staircase top, higher up than the hole which had let in the draught of air. When we examined the John Nash room, we found the point of it sticking through the plaster just above the top of the wainscoting. It would have spoiled the wainscoting if we had made a new door. We decided that for the present we'd leave the cellars with the trap door as the one way into them. As Clow said, they were of no use unless the Germans came—a most unlikely event. The main job in the John Nash room was the ceiling.

The ceiling proved to be one of the most difficult and exasperating of all our operations. It was split, and in the middle hung down about two feet from the horizontal.

This apparently had happened because of the weight of the central ornamental plaster moulding, most of which had fallen and could not be replaced. The cornice mouldings, however, were undamaged, and should remain so if we removed the broken plaster and the laths carefully.

The laths (thin strips of split chestnut an inch wide

and four feet long) were nailed grid-wise across the rafters. When we removed some of them, we found that it was the rafters themselves that had given way. Six of them had broken near the middle of the ceiling and were held only by the laths that joined them to the unbroken ones.

They *were* rafters, and not the floor joists of the room above. The ceiling in fact was a false ceiling. Between it and the floor above, which happened to be that of our own bedroom, was a clear space of four feet. We saw that the only way to repair the broken rafters was to take up some of the bedroom floor boards, heave up the broken ends one by one until they were horizontal again, and secure them with battens to the joists of the bedroom floor.

Dain was a little dismayed when I told her about the floor boards, for it meant moving the bedroom furniture and taking up some of the lino we had already laid. I assured her, with an optimism which, alas, was not justified, that it would be a simple matter, and that the boards would soon be back. Actually, it took me nearly a day to remove them, for they were very thick and secured with enormous nails.

One could not do a job like this quietly, nor could it be done without making a considerable mess. The plaster itself was nearly three inches thick. When it fell it disintegrated into a fine white powder, which rose in choking clouds, and, when we opened the door, was swept by the draught all over the house and settled like fine snow on the floors and furniture.

It was difficult for Dain and Parkey to carry on with

145

the nursery school in these circumstances, but once started we could not stop. Unfortunately, the weather was cold and rainy, and the children could not go down to the quarry. We all had to make the best of it.

It took us three days to brace up the broken rafters— three days of almost continual hammering. It took another morning to restore the bedroom floor boards. Then we had to cut round the ceiling cornices, remove all the remaining horizontal plaster and the laths. There were many hundreds of these laths, each with four nails which, being rusted, would not draw with pincers and had to be hammered till they broke, and each blow with the hammer re-agitated the plaster dust. Yet the nails had to be removed so that the plaster boards, which Eddie had procured for us, could be fixed snugly to the rafters.

The boards were made of plaster of Paris sandwiched between thin cardboard. They measured eight feet by four. They were heavy and extremely brittle, and each one had to be held flat and accurately placed against the rafters before it could be nailed. On a vertical wall this would have been easy enough; on a ceiling it was the devil, for the only way to hold it was to stand on stepladders and hold it with our heads until all but the last nails were in.

All of us suffered in some degree. I was very sympathetic with Dain, Parkey and Porgy for what they had to endure with the noise and mess. They were missing the worst of it, however.

There were times during the fixing of the boards when I could almost have wept from exasperation and sheer fatigue, for up to the last one the powder and dust continued to fall and rise as we hammered, getting into our eyes, choking us. It was on our clothes, on our hair and skin. We looked like snowmen.

Several times, while pressing a board up with my head, holding a nail with one hand and the hammer in the other, I struck my hand instead of the nail itself. Once I got cramp while on the top of the stepladder, and only a miraculous reach over by Clow saved me from falling with the board on my head. Yet, apart from an occasional *jowl*, Clow never once complained. He was exceeding himself in geniality. Whenever I gave vent to my feelings, he'd grin and say:

"Now we'll soon have it done, and it will look beautiful then. The best room in the house. You'll be proud of it. When you get it cleaned up and painted and your furniture in, and the lamps lit and a nice fire going, it will look every bit as good as in the old days. Only keep the children out of it. Keep it for your best."

It was done in the end. The last board was nailed. There was no more dust to come down. Clow expertly filled in the joints between the boards and the old cornices with new plaster. We gave the whole ceiling two coats of white distemper, filled in one or two cracks in the vertical walls, and distempered them a pale warm grey. The fireplace from the library was fitted, and I did not grudge Clow the honour of being the first to light it. It was wide enough to burn logs. It worked perfectly. Nor did I grudge him taking the credit for having done the whole job himself, which he did unblushingly.

"I told you I could do it, and make it look nice," he said when, after we had swept the floor and removed the ladders and tools, Dain came to see it. "God knows what the contractors would have done with it, and God knows what they would have charged—and they'd have taken at least a month for the job!"

"It's simply lovely!" was Dain's enthusiastic comment, but she added almost as enthusiastically: "And isn't it nice to think there'll be no more dust and hammering."

Fortunately, Clow did not seem to think that it was within his province to tell us how to decorate and furnish the room. I was indeed worried as to what he would think of our furniture, which certainly wasn't up to "squire" standard. Probably he would have liked to see it all Chippendale or Queen Anne walnut. We had a small Queen Anne tallboy which was in style with the room, but everything else—including a chair I had made from the elm slabs of a blacksmith's bellows and a table I had made from the planks of an old sailing ship in our early hard-up Cornish days—was either modern or non-period: two divans, three upholstered lounge chairs, and some carved wood stools I had acquired in Africa.

We had one good Chinese carpet, some Kelim rugs and a huge rust-red and yellow-striped Saharan rug (souvenir of an unlucky filming expedition I had once gone with to Timbuktu), which would do for a window curtain to draw across the shutters at night.

We painted the panels of the wainscoting and doors cream, with their surrounds dark but warm grey, picking out the narrow moulding of the surrounds with gilt, and doing the same with the carved cupboard doors. Clow took no hand in this. We did it in the evening when the younger children were in bed, Porgy, Parkey and Amelia helping. I made a three-shelved bookcase out of the quarry planks that Eddie had sawn for us, to reach along the whole of one wall. On the top shelf we placed a small carving by Barbara Hepworth (souvenir of a period when I had shared a house with her and John Skeaping in St John's Wood, before either of them had become famous), the silver candlestick, and some large pots that would hold flowers when we could get them.

I fancied that Clow would have liked to have seen ancestral portraits on the walls, some sporting prints, perhaps a fox's mask and brushes, and other trophies of the chase. We had an Ethel Walker seascape, done at my native Yorkshire village, and Turneresque in its glowing blues and greys, some coloured chalk drawings of antelope by John Skeaping, and two Medici Society facsimile reproductions of British Museum Chinese prints.

It wasn't Regency and it wasn't John Nash and it wasn't squire, and maybe there was a touch of artistic snobbery in it (for most of us are snobs of some sort). It was pleasing to look at anyway. It was warm and comfortable and cosy, and in the evenings, for us adults and for the elder children up to their bedtime, a sanctuary. Here we could entertain any of our rapidly-growing circle of friends to tea and sometimes to supper. Eddy called whenever his business (but not yet another birthday) brought him into the district, and sometimes he brought his very charming wife.

Tom (Jew's Harp) drove Mother out one Sunday afternoon. To Timothy's delight she brought Nellie with her. She wore a heavy black silk dress with fine lace collar, in Victorian style, and, sitting in one of our easy chairs in front of the fire—this after she'd been shown all over the house—she looked magnificent.

She was full of praise for what we had done to the place. When I told her that we owed it nearly all to Clow, she was indignant.

"Rubbish! He'd like to think so. That man still thinks he's the squire of Castle Druid. He's only a common workman and he gives himself the airs of a duke. It's you and your lady who have made all this so nice."

Thank heaven that Clow didn't hear this.

Actually, Clow himself seemed very reluctant to look at the room when we had put the finishing touches to it. When I persuaded him to do so, he would not advance beyond the threshold, his excuse being that he didn't want to damage the carpet or rugs with his heavy working boots. He doffed his hat, and stood looking as self-conscious as he had done when he had given us the Christmas parcel. All he could say when he had glanced round the room was:

"Very nice. You've got it very tidy."

I had got our radio to work, and here in the John Nash room, while Dain and Porgy and Parkey busied themselves with knitting and sewing, we could hear the news, and, as an antidote, listen to the incomparable Tommy Handley. And here, when all had gone to bed and there was relative quiet (the babies didn't as a rule start yelling till 2 a.m.) I would open my typewriter and try and get on with the half-finished novel I had abandoned at the outbreak of the war—for the need of money was daily growing more urgent.

It wasn't easy. Physically I was working all out from early morning till dusk—at the field fences, making or repairing gates, clearing clumps of gorse, sometimes with Clow, sometimes on my own, if he was engaged upon a job which didn't need my co-operation. I had started on the preparation of a large vegetable garden, which we had decided to make on level ground at the bottom of the meadow near the stream. I had to remove all the turf before I could start digging, and enclose the whole patch with a stock-proof fence.

We were told that there were foxes in the neighbourhood. That meant a wire-netting run for our poultry. I had to make coops for the chicks we had bought, and then a larger house for the time when they had grown. I enjoyed doing all this, and only wished I had the strength and energy to have done twice as much. My resources of both were limited.

With the room so warm and cosy, my mind just would not work, and after composing perhaps a sentence or two, I'd fall asleep.

11

SPRING WAS coming. The days were getting longer. There were golden catkins on the trees down by the stream. The children had found snowdrops and the green shoots of daffodils in the sheltered woods. In the tall horse chestnuts near the house, a colony of noisy rooks were building their untidy nests, making a din that was certainly as noisy as our hammering had been.

I'd had a visit from the Cultivation Officer of the County War Agricultural Committee—a panel of farmers and experts whose function was to put into effect all the Government schemes for producing the maximum amount of home-grown food. It offered expert technical advice to those who asked for it. It controlled a pool of agricultural machinery (largely "lease-lend" from America) that could be hired out at reasonable terms. It paid the various grants and subsidies that the Government awarded for ploughing up new land and growing certain crops, such as potatoes. It had authority to make financial loans to needy farmers for the purchase of fertilisers, seed, even of stock, to order farmers as to what crops they should grow, and—very important—to displace farmers who were not doing their job efficiently.

The officer was an intelligent and agreeable young Welshman. He was a farmer's son and had won a university scholarship and a degree in agriculture, and he was a disciple of Professor Stapleton, the famous authority on land reclamation, whose radio talks on this subject had fascinated me before the war.

We walked together round the whole farm. He prodded the soil in every field, looked closely at the wild grasses that were growing on the parts free from bracken and gorse. He was not very optimistic, but he was not completely discouraging. Apart from the meadow near the house, it was all poor land, he said—made poorer by years of neglect. He trusted that I wasn't hoping to make a living out of it.

Yet much poorer land than this had been made productive since the Government had realised how important it was to grow more food. There was, he said, a fair amount of humus in the soil. The ideal thing would be to plough it and sow it with good grass and make a permanent pasture of it, as had been done so successfully on many of the Welsh hills. This would be very expensive, however, and it would be several years before there would be any substantial return on the outlay. In any case, the Government insisted on cereal and animal fodder crops at present, with a certain acreage of potatoes. What we must do therefore (and he emphasised the *must*) was to plough all the hill fields, about thirty acres, sow twenty of them with a hardy strain of oats, six with roots—swedes or mangolds—and the remaining four with potatoes. With that and the hay from the meadow and the supplementary rations we should be allowed to buy, we ought to be able to keep four dairy cows and sell the milk to the Milk Marketing Board. It would be a small, but appreciable, contribution to the war effort.

I thought that I had better be quite frank with the officer. I told him that I hadn't had much experience of farming, and that my capital was small. I hadn't expected to make a living out of the farm. I wanted to do it because any sort of reclamation had always fascinated me, and because I wanted to do anything I could to beat Hitler. I couldn't afford to lose much money.

I asked him if he could give me a rough idea of what my total outlay would be.

He laughed. That wasn't easy, but he'd do his best. There was a horrible silence while he scribbled in his notebook. Then he said:

"I can only give you a very approximate idea, for it's not my department, but allowing for the ploughing-up grant, the subsidy on lime, and the extra grant of £10 an acre for potatoes, it would be somewhere between four hundred and five hundred pounds. That of course wouldn't cover the cost of harvesting. You can sell your crops then, the Government definitely buys all your potatoes, and get some of your money back, but that would be bad farming. Apart from potatoes your cash crop should be either milk or meat. If you don't buy milkers, you should buy some store cattle and fatten them for selling. Good milkers will cost anything between sixty and a hundred pounds apiece. Store cattle, depending on their age and quality, from twenty pounds."

I was bothered. Our capital was now under six hundred pounds. We still owned Adder Howe, our Yorkshire home, and were getting a small rent for it. But we still owed five hundred pounds on the Castle Druid mortgage. I knew it was customary for farmers to get loans from their banks, just as tradesmen did for the buying of stock. I also knew that bank managers were shrewd people who never took risks. They required security for their loans, and must be assured that they'd get all their money back with interest and within a stated period.

When we got to the end of our tour, I asked the officer if there was a chance of the Committee helping me financially. He was not encouraging. They would only recommend a loan to established professional farmers who could prove that they required the money to increase the efficiency and productivity of their farms. There would be no doubt about the ploughing-up and the potato grants. I must realise that even for a professional farmer there would be a risk in cultivating my thirty acres. I would probably get good crops the first year. It didn't follow that I should harvest them successfully. A wet summer might mean that I shouldn't harvest them at all. Farming was a gamble, and no one knew it better than the War Agricultural Committee.

Deliberately I had arranged for the officer to come on a day when Clow was working on his own holding. Late that night, when Porgy and Parkey had gone to bed, leaving us to ourselves in the John Nash room, I told Dain what had happened.

"It certainly is an awful lot of money to pay out," she

said, "but we've got to do it whether we like it or not, and we do want to, anyway. We've got enough to pay for it, and we'll get it back by having cows and selling the milk, like other farmers do. Look at the Jew's Harp farm. That's only small, yet they can keep six cows as well as calves and pigs. We ought to have pigs. And more poultry. We mustn't think about having a failure with the crops. Of course we'll be able to harvest them. It isn't often there's a wet summer, and if it did happen, we can raise money on Adder Howe, although we must never sell it. I'd hate to think we were never going back to Yorkshire, much as I like Wales."

Although her optimism was warming, it did not allay my fears.

"I think," I said, "that we'll have to manage without Clow soon. If we get the committee or a contractor to do all the ploughing and sowing, we shan't really need his help."

She was shocked. "Oh. We just can't finish with Clow. We shall need him when it comes to hay time and harvest. And there's still a lot of fencing to do, isn't there? And there's the stable roof. If we get more ponies, we'll need the stable. And there's the dam wall for the lake. Have you forgotten about the lake? We'll never be able to get anyone half so good as Clow. What a pity we couldn't do all the farming with him and ourselves. We could, you know, if we had a horse, and it would be more fun than having it all done for us with machinery."

It might be more fun, I thought, and by fun I knew that Dain meant the pleasure and satisfaction we had always found in making and doing things with our own hands. It was more fun making a bookcase than buying one in a shop, more fun knitting a jersey or weaving a rug, or building a chicken house, making our own garden. We couldn't cultivate thirty acres of land with a spade, nor would it have been practical (or even possible) to have done it with a horse and horse-drawn implements. Even the Jew's Harp (although they owned a light carthorse) had most of their ploughing, mowing and reaping done by tractor, and used their horse only for leading manure and more leisurely work.

As for the stable, there was no necessity and certainly no urgency for this. I saw no prospect of our being able to afford more ponies. The lake, desirable though it seemed, would be still more of a luxury, and we might have to defer that until after the war. How simple everything would be if we had adequate capital. If only I could get on with my writing, finish my novel, and that, when published, it would make a lot of money.

I had another shot at the book when Dain had gone to bed, but I could not concentrate on it. I kept thinking about Clow, about the money I should have to give him if we kept him on, and save if we didn't. I wondered whether if I explained my financial situation to him he would take less, or perhaps work for us only part-time. Even this would be more than we could afford if we were to carry out the cultivation programme practically ordered by the officer. No. There seemed to be no alternative. Clow must go. I must break it to him in the morning, and it was going to be a hateful task. For, apart from all practical considerations, I'd grown very fond of him.

*   *   *

We were still working when the weather permitted, as it did that fateful next morning, on the boundary fence between the top fields and the open common. The fence consisted of old thorn interspersed with a few stunted ash trees. Thorn and ash were too overgrown for laying. We had to lop the tops and use the trunks as posts for barbed wire, putting cut stakes from the copses where there were gaps.

Clow had come straight to the job, not calling at the house, and he had started work when I joined him. It was not his habit to wish me good morning. This time he did and with a smile. It was clear that he was in an unusually happy mood, which did not encourage me in the unhappy task I was bracing myself to perform.

He had been chopping at a thick ash bole with his long-shafted timber axe, and he stopped work and stood with his hands clasped on the handle butt.

"Well," he said genially, "and how did you get on with the man from the committee? I saw him walking with you up and down the fields, sniffing at this and that." His smile became sarcastic.

"*Jowl*, I suppose he was full of knowledge. They all are, these grand gentlemen from the towns, with nothing to do but drive round in nice motor cars and tell farmers how to do their jobs."

I knew better than to defend the officer. Clow at least had given me a lead for the disagreeable subject I had to discuss with him.

"We got on all right," I said. "He looked at every field,

but he seemed to think that apart from the big pasture it was all poor land, and that if it wasn't for the war the best thing to do with it would be to break it up and sow it with grass, make permanent grazing on it. His committee wouldn't agree to that, however. I've got to plough thirty acres, sow twenty of them with oats, six with roots or kale, four with potatoes. It's going to be a very expensive business. It's all got to be limed and spread with fertilisers. On top of that, I've got to buy milkers or store cattle. To tell you the truth, Clow, I don't know how I'm going to do it on top of my other expenses. I just haven't got the money unless I cut down in other directions."

Did he guess what I was leading up to? He was no longer smiling, but eyeing me very earnestly.

"*Jowl*, I could have told you what the land needed, and how to make it pay, too. Who's going to do the job, and what are they going to charge?"

"The committee, or a private contractor. He said that after deducting the ploughing-up grant and the potato subsidy, the whole thing would cost between four and five hundred pounds, without stock, of course.

He was thoughtful for a moment. Then:

"You've got to lay down money for farming, but it wouldn't cost half as much as that if you did it yourself. These Government experts! They're only out to get as much money as they can out of you."

I didn't believe this, but I didn't protest, and Clow went on:

"Take no notice of the damned Government. All this would make a grand little farm if you set about it in the right way. What you need is a tractor and implements of

159

your own, and not have to get outsiders to do it and charge you what they like."

"But how could I afford a tractor? That would mean putting down almost as much money for a start. I tell you that I simply haven't got it."

I paused. The dreaded moment had come. It took me all my courage to look Clow in the face and then say:

"As a matter of fact, I had decided to tell you this morning that as I'll have to lay down the money for the farm I'll have to stop having you work for me. And I can't tell you how sorry I am, for you've done a wonderful job for us. I know that no one could have done it so well, or been more reasonable about payment. You've been splendid, and my wife thinks the same. If we had the money, we'd like to have you working for us permanently. As we haven't—there it is."

I felt tears swelling into my own eyes, but I saw none in Clow's. He was smiling.

"*Jowl,*" he said, quite calmly. "It's funny you should say all that, for I've been trying to make up my mind for a time now, to have things out with you. I don't like prying into other people's business, but I have my eyes open. You've spent a lot of money on the place since you came here, apart from what you paid me—although I've charged you fair, maybe half of what you'd have had to pay anyone else. But I've noticed several times when you've been paying me up, that you've looked a bit anxious. I like a man to be honest, and you've been honest with me, and I'm glad you've been straight as to how things are with you. But you've no need to get worried about giving me the sack. I've been going to tell you for some weeks past that we ought to have a different arrangement."

I was puzzled. I hadn't expected anything like this, and I didn't know what to say.

"Now listen," he went on. "You've been straight with me, and I'll be straight with you. I've told you about my sister Rosie who married a Canadian in the first war and now lives in Canada . . ."

"Who sent you the parcel at Christmas?"

"Yes, indeed. Never once has she forgotten since she went, and it's more than twenty years since I've seen her. She was going to pay a visit here just before the second war started, but her husband had an illness and she couldn't come. I didn't tell you that although he had plenty of money he was a stingy devil, a real miser. Well, just a few weeks ago I had a letter from her to say he'd passed on, and yesterday I got another letter from her. He's left her all his money, and although she still doesn't know how much it is, it must be a lot. She's sent me a cheque for a tidy sum."

I was still puzzled.

"I'm glad to hear that," I said.

"Yes, yes. But wait. I haven't told you all yet. I've been telling her all about Castle Druid, and what we've done to the place, and about you and your missus and the little ones, and she's very pleased about everything, for she says it's all helping to beat the Germans. She's going to send some food and clothes for the little ones. But more than anything, she's pleased about the farm. I told her that you were going to clear and cultivate all the land. She hates the Germans like mad. Her three boys were killed in the first war, remember. The more food we grow in this country, she says, the quicker we'll beat them."

This was all very dramatic, but apart from my mind being relieved about the matter of telling Clow that we couldn't keep him on, I was deriving no special comfort from it. What was he getting at ?

Suddenly he took his pay book from his pocket, opened it, and took from between the leaves a very faded photograph, and handed it to me.

"That's Rosie," he said, "as she was before she got wed. She'll look different now, of course—and it doesn't show the colour of her hair."

It was a conventional studio photograph, head and shoulders, of a young girl. She was smiling, showing a fine set of teeth. Her hair was wavy, light, and I could believe that a colour photograph would have shown it gold. There was in the shape of her face, in the set of her eyes, a faint, but definite, resemblance to Clow himself. It was a beautiful face. There was character in it, and there was dignity and breeding.

"She's very lovely," I said, and I saw that there were tears in Clow's eyes now, as he took it back and put it carefully away.

"Yes, indeed. There wasn't a lovelier girl in Wales than Rosie. And she had a beautiful voice too. If she hadn't met the man she married, she'd have been famous on the stage. She'll have lost her beauty now. Well, you may see her some day, for she says in her letter that she's coming over for her holiday when the war's finished."

"That will be very nice for you," I said. "We'll be very

162

pleased to meet her."

"Yes, indeed. And she's going to get a surprise when she sees what we've done to the old place, only I hope by that time we'll have all the front painted, and the stable roof put right, and the garden made, and the lake too, as it was, for although she never saw it except in ruins, she heard plenty about it from my father. But it's the farm she wants to see, and the cows in the cowhouse, and stock on the land, and everything looking well. And she's not going to see that unless you go about it in the right way, so let's get down to business. What about my going in with you on the job? Don't say anything yet. Just listen to what I have to tell you."

I didn't say anything. I was too surprised.

"Listen. I'm going to buy a tractor and implements with the money Rosie has sent me. In her letter she says I'm wasting my time doing a mason's job, and that when I've finished with you I ought to do farming only. But what can I do with my eight acres of land? What's she's sent me is not enough to buy another farm and stock it, and there's not another farm for sale or let within twenty miles of here that's any good. With a tractor, I can do my own piece without hiring a horse and implements as I've done in the past. I can do all your land, and make a bit contracting—for everyone is short of help round here, with so many young men being called up for the war. I'd do your fields like any other contractor, if you wanted, and charge you less. But what I'd like to do is to come in with you. If you're short of money, I've enough now to buy a couple of milkers, and we can buy feed for them until they go out to grass."

I was stunned.

"You mean a partnership?"

"Why not? We'd both put into it what we could afford, and share the profits according. We'd reckon our own time so much an hour, the same as other expenses, but instead of you paying me each week, as you have been doing, we'd just keep an account of it to be set down and balanced up at the end of each quarter."

I hesitated.

"You've taken me by surprise, Clow," I said. "I'll have to think it over and discuss it with my wife. It would be for the farm only, of course."

"Yes, indeed. With the use of the cowhouse and other farm buildings. I'd like to put the stable roof to rights, though. It will be a month, maybe, before I get the tractor, and that would be mine, just as the land and buildings would be yours. We ought to get all the fences finished by then, but once you'd made up your mind about things, there'd be nothing more to pay me. And I'll tell you what. I'd like to see the wall for the lake built. The days are getting longer now, and we could do it in the evenings maybe. It would be a beautiful thing, the lake. Just what the mansion needs to show it off. Have you thought any more about having a water-wheel? Have you walked down the Cwm yet to Dai the Mill? Dai's not a miller. He calls himself a poet and he's a bit soft in the head. The grindstones have been taken away but the wheel's still there, and I think he'd be glad enough to sell it to you cheap. You could make electricity with it, and maybe grind your corn into flour if you bought a hammer mill."

I knew about the old mill, for the man who had sold us Castle Druid had mentioned it, but I had firmly resisted the temptation to walk down the valley and see it and its owner. Was Clow deliberately tempting me now? Could I trust him about this proposition of a partnership? Unpopular though he was, no one had made the slightest imputation as to his honesty. In all our dealings he had been straight.

It was not an unreasonable proposition. I would have liked to have done the whole thing myself— ploughing, harrowing, sowing. I'd had a little experience of tractor ploughing on our Yorkshire land, taking lessons with my neighbour. But I was an amateur. In any case, I could not afford a tractor, and if I could, the expense of it would not be justified for a farm as small as Castle Druid.

Was Clow himself a competent farmer? We had by this time visited his holding. His cottage was small, but everything was as clean and tidy as any woman would have kept it. The cowshed he had built was light and airy, the pigsties and other outbuildings all in perfect condition. So were all his fields. It had puzzled me, how he had time to do it all on top of his other activities. He was an amazing man. I had no real doubt that he would be able to run Castle Druid as well as any other man would do it, certainly better than I would. As to finance, I had been prepared to lose money. If he thought we could make some, that would clinch the matter.

Yet I was aware of a vague uneasiness. Who was going to be boss, Clow or I?

"It seems all right," I said guardedly, "but I'll need to

think it over and discuss it with my wife."

He laughed.

"Of course. But there it is. Let's get on with the old fence and we'll talk about it tomorrow, but don't say anything to the Government chap until we do."

12

DAIN THOUGHT that it was a splendid idea, that it was the luckiest thing that could have happened. She was certain that we could trust Clow. She was certain that I'd been wrong in even thinking of giving him notice. The way he ran his own holding was a proof that he understood farming. How exciting to be able to have cows straight away, even if they were only half ours. She and Porgy would be able to do the milking, and make butter too.

She was glad that Clow had suggested doing the stable roof. Even if we didn't get any more ponies yet, we'd need it when we did, and if the farm made money, and the school made money too, as it might do if we got more paying pupils, we'd have to get at least one more pony, for parents liked the idea of their children being taught to ride. And she did agree with Clow about the lake making the place look beautiful. We ought to start clearing the part that would be flooded at once, although she hoped it wasn't going to be dangerous for the children. We'd have to have it all properly fenced.

Such optimism was contagious, and although I still had misgivings, I saw no strong reason for not accepting Clow's proposition. We'd need some form of contract, of course, and probably that would have to be prepared by a solicitor.

We shook hands on it next day. Clow agreed that we should have a deed drawn up by a solicitor, that we should have a joint account at a bank, and, for a start, each pay into it the sum of £250. We'd buy two milkers as soon as the deed was signed, and fodder to keep them; and start ploughing as soon as we got the tractor. In the meantime we could carry on with the fencing and clearing of the remaining clumps of furze in the fields that were to be ploughed.

But my conscience troubled me about the lake. It was going to take time and a certain amount of money, and we must not spend either just to make the place look beautiful. Directly or indirectly, it must help the war effort. The fact that I wanted it so much for my personal delight did not help to ease my conscience.

It had been one of my life-long ambitions to own a trout stream, dam it and make a lake in which trout would fatten and multiply. There had been a little stream close to our Cornish hut. We had dammed it where it ran through our flower garden, making an ornamental pond round which we had planted irises. The stream was too small for trout. We had put some goldfish in the pond, but they hadn't been there a week before a heron from the creek discovered them, and ate them all, and in our first summer both stream and pond dried up.

The stream of our Yorkshire home had contained trout. Indeed, it was in its lower reaches, close to the sea, where the old mill was built, that I had poached my first fish with a ha'penny hook and grocer's string for a line, a hazel wand for rod. It was the miller's dam which swarmed with fat trout (strictly preserved by the squire who owned the mill) that had first roused my ambition to own a stream with a pool.

The stretch of the stream that we had acquired, however, was near its source on the moors. Except in floods, the volume of water in it was small. Its bottom was rocky, giving no hold for the waterweeds which trout favour as a hunting ground for snails. It would have cost almost as much as a house to build a wall across it and make even a fair-sized pool.

The Castle Druid stream, although not big enough to drive a water wheel directly, had twice the volume of our Yorkshire one. Its bed was gravel and sand, and there was watercress and other aquatic weeds growing at its fringes. By turning the stones, the children had already found trout up to six inches in length. There could be little doubt that if we made the lake, these trout would find even more abundant food, and would grow very fast—for the size of most fish is proportionate to the amount of food they obtain, particularly if they can find it without much effort.

Would I be justified in making the lake so that it would produce food in the shape of fish? Certainly that would be more patriotic than doing it merely to enhance the beauty of our home. My conscience said no. Trout, like pheasants and oysters, was a luxury food. Under the most favourable conditions it would take at least a couple of years for the stream trout to grow into pounders, and even then I'd have to catch them in the conventional (and highly pleasant) way, with rod and fly or worm. It would almost be sacrilege to catch them with a net. No, the only justification for doing it would be for the same purpose as my Yorkshire miller's dam had been built—as a reservoir for the driving of a wheel, for grinding corn, or, to be more modern, for generating electricity. In fact it would be justified if we could just make electricity to light the mansion. At present we were entirely dependent upon candles and paraffin for illumination, both made from petroleum, imported at the risk of sailors' lives.

We must not start work on the dam wall unless it was certain that we would be able to acquire a waterwheel. The excitement of doing it, the aesthetic pleasure, the trout—all these must be secondary motives; and I was not at all sure that, even with the waterwheel, I was not doing a little twisting with my conscience. The fact that I had always dreamt of having one was suspicious.

Dain helped me to overcome my scruples.

"We must go down and have a look at the old mill we heard about," she said. "The waterwheel mightn't be any good. It wasn't certain that the man who owned it wanted to sell it. If he did, he might want too much money. In any case it would be a nice walk, and it would be fun going somewhere we hadn't been before."

It wasn't just because I'd been afraid of temptation

169

that I'd refrained from going to the mill. We had been so busy all winter with the house and the land, there had been no time for walks. Apart from what we saw on our way to Castlebridge, we had seen very little beyond our own boundaries.

We chose a Saturday afternoon for our expedition, and we took Annabella (saddled) and just our own children, leaving Porgy and Parkey in charge of the rest. This in itself was conducive to putting us all in good humour. The weather helped too. It was mid-March and a dry warm day with the sun shining. It was so good, I felt, to be on our own again. To hear the clop clop of Annabella's hooves on the road. To have our children (save Tim who was riding) running ahead, finding primroses, looking not so successfully, for birds' nests.

There was a path down the stream below our land, but we kept to the road, here little more than a lane, which rose from our valley and then levelled, running parallel to the course of the stream, giving us a fine view of the country, with the bare hills to the north of us, and, far to the south, across flatter, cultivated land, a glimpse of the land-locked sea at Milford Haven.

The sight of the sea gave me a little pang of homesickness.

"This country is good," I said, "but it's not as good as our own, and it isn't as good as Cornwall, least not that part of it where we lived. What's wrong with Castle Druid is that it's too far from the sea. No boats, no fishing, no driftwood to be picked up from the beach after a storm."

Dain took the defensive.

"I wish we were nearer the sea, too. But even at Adder Howe we were a long way away from it, and don't forget that it was all shut off by barbed wire because of the invasion scare, and we were not allowed to go on any of the beaches. And it will be like that until the war is over. It wouldn't have been so bad if they hadn't shut off the moors too."

The moors, which extended for many miles from the boundaries of our land at Adder Howe, had been a big compensation for not being able to live actually on the sea's edge, as we had done in Cornwall. They had a unique beauty and fascination. You were free to walk or ride over them wherever you wished. The War Office had taken over the whole area as a battle-training ground, and public entry was strictly forbidden.

"You know," I said, "Cornwall would take some beating. Think of our little cove, almost at our front door, always sheltered, no matter what the weather; and our motor boat and dinghy; and fishing, and swimming in summertime. The blue sea in summer. Those coves along the coast where you could land and make driftwood fires. Do you remember . . ."

"Stop it!" she protested. "You're making me feel homesick. Of course I remember. It was all so lovely. But so was Adder Howe, and so is this, really. If we haven't got the sea, we've got the country, and if we make the lake, it will be almost as good as having the cove at our front door, especially if we have fish in it. And couldn't we have some sort of a boat? We can swim in it in summer, and if there's a shallow end with a sandy beach, the little children can have it for paddling. It will be perfect if we do get the waterwheel. I think that as well as using it for electricity, we ought to grind flour with it. If we grew just a little wheat, we could grind that, and actually make our own bread from start to finish. We could make oatmeal anyway, so that we wouldn't have to buy it in the shops. It would all be helping win the war."

Clow had given us directions for finding the mill, which was about two miles downstream from Castle Druid. We were to take the first turn on our right from the main road. Soon the elder children came running back to tell us that they had found the lane. They at once dashed ahead again, and were out of sight when we came to it. They wanted to be the first to see the wheel. We followed, at Annabella's easy walking pace, downhill.

The lane, which was only roughly metalled, meandered between high banks which shut off our view of the country. We had gone maybe half a mile when we entered a wood and caught sight of the stream again, not much bigger than where it ran through our own land. Then, round another bend, we saw Amelia running towards us, looking very excited.

"We've seen it! We've seen it! And there's ever such a nice old man. He looks just like Father Christmas. He's given us some apples. Come on. Do hurry and look at it. A real waterwheel, but it isn't going."

As we turned the bend, we saw a cottage with some tumbledown outbuildings. Alongside the nearest of them, which had no roof, was an ancient-looking, overshot iron waterwheel. Near the wheel, which I observed even then had an ash sapling growing between its spokes, like the one that had grown from the bulging wall of our mansion, stood Jane and Angus, each munching an apple, and an old man with a long white beard and whiskers, who touched his hat and smiled genially as we approached. Except that he was short and very thin, and that his clothes were black, like those of a clergyman, he did look like the traditional Father Christmas, with something, too, of George Bernard Shaw and Augustus John. His cheeks—what you could see of them above the whiskers, were rosy, and he had twinkling blue eyes and a soft musical voice.

"Good day to you, lady. Good day to you, sir," he greeted us. "You're the English folk from the mansion? I've heard all about you from Albert the Post. And about the great improvements you've done to the old place. Well, well, indeed. I'm glad that you have come to call, although I can't offer you any hospitality whatever, except an apple, maybe—for I've no woman in the house."

We shook hands with him. His hands were white and he didn't look a bit like a miller, but I said to him:

"You're Dai the Miller, aren't you?" He smiled.

"Miller? No. They call me Dai the Mill only because I live in the old mill cottage. That is our Welsh way of speaking to avoid confusion. My father was the miller here many years ago. He did not wish me to be a miller. He wished me to be a preacher and he sent me to college. But I didn't want to be a preacher either. I wished to be a poet, and a poet I am. When my good father died, he left me the mill and a little money to live on. Why should a poet work, except at his poetry, and read books and study nature and the beautiful things of life like the trees and birds and flowers. I am told that you are a writer yourself."

Remembering my first conversation with Eddy on this subject, I said guardedly:

"Yes, in a way. But not poetry. And I've been farming since the war."

"Ah—and you'd write in English, of course. There is only one language for poetry, and that is Welsh. Do you know any Welsh?"

"No—only a few words like *Ody* and *jowl*. But the children are learning Welsh at school."

"That's good. That's good. It's a beautiful language, like music itself. Now, how would you describe in English the sound that a stream makes running slowly among the rocks in the wood down there, with a blackbird singing at the same time?"

He didn't give me a chance to try, for he raised one hand in a preacher's gesture and said:

"Listen now."

He recited what I took to be a verse of poetry. I didn't understand a word of it, yet the words themselves, the rhythm and lilt of his voice, did evoke for me the sound of running water, the singing of a bird. The children had listened spell-bound.

"That sounded lovely," I said with sincerity, but with a secret misgiving. It would be embarrassing if we were going to have to listen to a full-length recital of Welsh poetry. There was something of the Ancient Mariner in this extraordinary man.

"Was that your own poetry?" I asked.

He gave a dangerous smile.

"Yes indeed, but that is one verse only." And then, to my relief, he added: "But it would be no good giving you the whole poem if you do not understand our language.

"Are your poems published?" (And I nearly said, remembering Eddy: Do you write under your own name?)

He laughed.

"No. Not yet. Someday, perhaps, I will have them published in one volume, but I do not worry about it. I write them because I like writing them."

"Please—don't you ever make the waterwheel go?"— It was Angus who had brought us down to earth.

We all laughed.

"We're very interested in waterwheels," I said quickly, in case the subject should be changed. "We've been thinking of installing one in Castle Druid, to use it for making electricity. Do you mind if I have a look at yours?"

"Not at all. Take a look at it while I go into the house and find some more apples. I will not ask you in, for it is very untidy, and I'd be shamed to let anyone see it."

There was a low wall between the road and the wheel itself. I climbed over it, and I looked at the wheel as excitedly as though it had been the latest model of a motor car at the Motor Show, and I a young man with money to burn.

It was fixed in a pit close up to the roofless mill building, so that only one half of it was visible. I had no ruler with me, but I roughly guessed its diameter at nine

175

feet, its width at four. It was old. The ash sapling that grew between (and would have effectively locked) its spokes, was at least twenty years old. The vanes which formed the buckets had been wood, and were nearly all rotted away, and there was only a vestige left of a wooden sluice and brackets on the mill wall, which had once fed the wheel from the stream itself, where apparently there had been no dam. But the body of the wheel was heavy cast iron, made up of sections—bolted and not riveted together. On the outer rim were grooves to take the wooden vanes. The iron was rusted, but in no visible place was it deeply corroded. With new vanes, the thing could be almost as good as new.

I saw that the power of the wheel had been transmitted to the mill by means of a spur, six feet in diameter, bolted to the spokes. The teeth of the spur engaged on those of a pinion, or cog-wheel, fixed on a steel shaft passing through the wall. I knew that an overshot water-wheel derives its power from the weight of water carried in its buckets from the point where they start to fill, to where they empty again on their downward course. The wheel therefore must revolve slowly, giving the buckets ample time to fill; for machinery requiring high revolutions (like a dynamo) one would need a system of gears from the main shaft.

"Is it all right?" asked Dain over the wall. She was holding Annabella, with Timothy still in the saddle. "It looks very rusty."

I answered excitedly, but keeping my voice low in case Dai should hear:

"It's all right. Wonderful. The rust is nothing. The

176

iron parts look perfectly sound. And it's not too big for us. It's in sections. We could take it to bits and rebuild it below our own dam when it's made. All we'll need are new vanes for the buckets, and we can make those from the quarry planks. If only he'll let us have it at a reasonable price. It must have cost at least a hundred pounds new."

At that moment Dai appeared again, with a small basket of apples in one hand, a sheaf of ominous-looking documents in the other. He offered an apple each to Dain and Timothy, and then to the rest of us, and then he put the basket down on the wall.

"You must take these back with you," he said. Then, holding up the documents:

"These are some of my poems, and I have had them typed and copies made, and perhaps the children would like to have them to read when they know the language well."

Amelia eagerly held out her hand for them.

"Thank you very much," she said politely, "How lovely."

I felt relieved again, for I thought we were in for another recital. I said to him:

"I've been looking at the old wheel with great interest."

He didn't look very interested himself.

"Yes?" he said, "It's all very tumbled down. It's a long time since it was working. I can hardly remember the time when it was."

"You're not thinking of ever making it work again, then?"

"No, indeed, why should I? I know nothing about mechanical things."

"Well," I said, "would you consider selling it to me?"

My heart was beating very fast.

"It's no good as it stands," I said, "but I think I could repair it, and that it would do for what I want. Will you sell it?"

Was I making a mistake in letting him see how keen I was? In my imagination I already saw the wheel rebuilt and installed below our dam wall; the wall built and the lake an actuality. We would have a sluice leading from a point about a foot lower than the level of the dam wall top, which would take the overflow from the lake, but fitted with a shutter, so that if the overflow were not enough to drive the wheel we could augment it. I could see the wheel turning, very slowly, but on the pinion shaft, and geared to it a whirring flywheel, and a belt leading round the pulley of a dynamo. I could imagine every room in Castle Druid being flooded with light at the flick of a switch, and all from the free and inexhaustible power of our stream.

Dai was smiling. If he'd been a hard businessman, I'd have known what that smile meant. He'd be thinking pleasantly of how he was going to take advantage of my keenness. Yet it would be worse, I thought, if, unlike a businessman, he wouldn't sell it at all.

He hadn't answered yet. He was still smiling. He was a poet, an artist. Perhaps the mill had an aesthetic and romantic value to him. There was nothing picturesque about it to my mind, but he might feel differently.

"We'd very much like to have it. The children are all

very excited about the idea of having a waterwheel." And I repeated:

"Will you sell it?"

He shook his head. My heart sank. But my disappointment was short-lived.

"No, I will not sell it. But it is no good to me whatever. I do not like mechanical things, and I would not keep anything another person wants. If you want the old wheel, you must have it. I am a poet."

13

I HAD no illusions about my partnership with Clow. I knew that I had never been cut out to be a businessman, and farming was a business, after all. True, that at one stage of my career, in the early post Kaiser-war days, discouraged by failure to win success as a writer, I had become a sharing partner with a family of inshore fishermen in my native Yorkshire village.

It hadn't been a formal partnership. There had been nothing in writing. The boat, a stout little motor coble, was theirs. I bought, or under their tuition made, my own gear, lines, nets, lobster pots; shared in the running expenses like fuel and bait; in the labour of hauling the boat; in the fishing itself. For this I took share in the very meagre profits. The most I ever made in one week was five pounds, when we had three lucky catches of salmon trout. The average for one year was thirty shillings a week.

It was in this period, however, that I conceived the idea of a collapsing metal lobster pot. This should have solved one of the inshore fishermen's biggest economic problems. Lobstering then was the most profitable of all their activities, for in this there was no competition with the steam trawler. But the pots used were homemade of wood, hazel wands, and manilla netting. They had to be ballasted. They were heavy, cumbersome, a dangerous load for a small boat when shifting grounds in bad weather. They were fragile too, and in a sudden storm, when it was impossible to lift them from the shallow rocky ground the lobsters favoured, they would be washed away, or so badly damaged as to need remaking.

My pot, although fundamentally of the same pattern as those that had been used on the coast for generations, was a quarter the weight. Its light steel galvanised frame was virtually indestructible. And when folded, six of them would take up the space of one of the old sort in a boat when shifting ground.

Tests undertaken by an inspector of the Ministry of Agriculture and Fisheries proved that my invention was all that I claimed for it.

I had seen in it, however, something more than a device to make our own fishing more profitable. If exploited properly, it might revolutionise the whole inshore fishing industry, not only in Great Britain but in all countries where lobsters were caught, for even in the States and Canada wooden pots were used, and the same conditions applied.

I had seen myself as a captain of industry, manufacturing the pots by mass production methods in an ideal factory. Organising the inshore fishing of my own country at least, specialising on lobsters and crabs (for which it was equally efficient) . . . starting a cannery to absorb catches in times of market glut.

It was when I took my first perfected and tested model to a hard-headed Birmingham manufacturer that disillusionment came. He believed everything I told him about its usefulness to fishermen. But where was my market for it? These inshore fishermen were poor on my own showing. Their own pots cost them only a few shillings for material to make, and their own time. My pot, even mass produced, would cost at least a pound to make, and the *selling* price should be at least 400 per cent of that. Would my poor fishermen pay £5 each for my patent lobster pots? No manufacturer would do it on his own. If I did it myself, I would need a capital of at least £20,000 to protect my patents and get the thing going. And the chances were I'd be throwing £20,000 down the drain.

I had gone back to writing, a wiser man, and my fishermen friends had solved their own economic problem by moving to a larger fishing port and investing their hard-won savings in a larger modern boat, which enabled them to use their old-fashioned non-collapsible pots in deeper, safer water.

I had no illusions that I was going to make a fortune out of farming. If things broke even at the end of our first year, I would be pleased. It was a war effort, the best I could do under the circumstances, and I could not do it without Clow.

Our deed of partnership was drawn up, signed and sealed. We opened our joint banking account. Clow, with a countersigned cheque on it, bought our first two dairy cows, a ton of hay, a ton of mangolds, and, on coupons we received from the committee, a ration of cake. We had fenced off the home pasture as a hayfield. The cows, and Annabella, and Clow's own heifers, were confined to the rough grazing up the valley of the stream, but the cows were in the cowshed at night.

Porgy and Dain did the milking. We took enough milk for our own use, and this was recorded in the partnership account which Porgy, having had experience of such things, kept for us. We had to buy two churns, and the balance of the milk was collected every morning by the truck of the Milk Marketing Board.

Clow bought his tractor. It was a reconditioned Fordson, with rubber-tyred wheels. With it went a three-furrow plough, a disc harrow, a roller and a trailer.

He ploughed his own fields first, and he wouldn't let me watch him for he hadn't driven a tractor for many years, and he needed to get his hand in. But he could not stop me watching when he began operations on my own land. He did not try, for he had got his hand in and he was full of self-confidence.

"*Jowl*," he boasted, after he had marked out the headlands of the first field. "I could drive one of these damn' things with my eyes shut. Nearly twenty years it is since I did plough—and then I was only at the job for a month or so, on a farm in the flat country down Tenby way. But I'd learnt to drive a tractor in South Africa. I was with a building contractor then, putting up a barn, and I wasn't getting on too well with the boss. The farmer had a tractor like this one, only brand new, and he'd sprained his wrist with the starting handle, so I started it for him. Just then the contractor boss came up and told me to be getting on with my own job, and I told him to go to hell. I'd have had my coat off to him if he'd given me any of his lip. The barn was nearly finished, and the farmer took me on, and I ploughed nearly a hundred acres for him. But we had an argument about something and I left him. Jump up now alongside me, and I'll show you how ploughing should be done. I'll make a better job of it than your bloody War Agricultural Committee, or anyone else round here."

He was giving orders again, and I was meekly taking them. I didn't mind. He drove the tractor down the middle of the field without hesitation, making a first triple furrow that seemed to me as straight as though it had been ruled. It was clear that once again Clow's swank was not just vanity. He was merely stating what was true. Besides, I was getting a private thrill out of it. The soil the plough was turning up had a rich brown colour. It smelled good. It was deeply exciting to think that this land which, like that we had ploughed up in Yorkshire, had lain unfruitful for so long, would produce crops again, and would go on producing.

I was itching to take a turn at the wheel myself. I daren't suggest it, however, and Clow didn't offer. When we reached the opposite headland he stopped and looked back at the furrows.

"Straight as a die, eh?" he said, "and the turf nicely buried. Couldn't be better. Well, I'll not be needing your help for this. You'd better get some more stakes cut for the fences. There's no time to waste if we're going to get everything done."

I had no doubt that in his own mind Clow did regard himself as the senior partner, the boss. It didn't seriously trouble me. He knew more about farming than I did. I was not in any sense afraid of him. If he became unpleasantly bossy, I could tell him so, and I could always remind him that, in spite of our deed of partnership, Castle Druid was mine.

The days were getting longer, and every hour of daylight, including Saturdays, we were working: Clow with his tractor on the fields, I at the fences or the garden or the poultry runs. We decided that, in addition to growing vegetables and producing eggs for our own use, we would engage in market gardening, and sell eggs to the Ministry of Food, which would entitle us to poultry ration coupons. This was outside our farming partnership, and the time I devoted to it was not entered in the partnership account, neither were the profits—if we ever made any.

Dain, Porgy and Parkey had their hands full with the children, whose numbers had now increased to twenty, excluding our own. The proportion of "payers" to "eight-and-sixers" was still unprofitable. We were losing money on them, and I was not certain that we were justified in buying two more riding ponies.

It was Eddy who told us about them. A friend of his on the coast of Cardiganshire ran a riding school. His house and stables and land, like our own in Yorkshire, had been requisitioned by the War Office for some sort of hush-hush research station. He was obliged to break up his stables, and we were offered two Welsh mountain ponies, both mares, and one of them in foal. They were ideal children's mounts, we were assured, and the price, with bridles and saddles, was only ten pounds apiece.

It was unfortunate that Eddy should disclose this information in the presence of the children, and that he should offer to run Dain and Amelia and Jane to see the ponies for themselves. They had been wild to go, and the result was a foregone conclusion. Bothered though I was at the bite out of our capital, I had to admit, when Snowdrop and Goldie eventually arrived, that they were worth the money, and I was almost convinced by Dain's argument that we might eventually make money out of them.

"They are mountain ponies, like Annabella," she said, "and they won't cost a farthing in food, except in very hard weather. The foal will be worth at least five pounds when it's two years old, and with them both being mares we should be able to go on breeding from them. It isn't as though they'll have to be stabled, although it would be nice to have the stable ready for them for next winter anyway, just in case we do get bad weather."

The stable roof was still unmended. I was glad (in spite of Clow's offer to do it) that the new ponies did not make its repair urgent, for there was the dam and the waterwheel to be done in any time we could spare from

185

farming. I thought that as we were working so hard during the week, we could at least use our Sundays for this, and Clow, when he had finished the ploughing, agreed.

I was determined that in the actual designing of the dam wall and its construction, I was going to be the authority. I'd need Clow's labour and skill in the actual building, but that was all. It had nothing to do with the farm, although it would be an asset if we could have the cowshed illuminated with electricity, and, if the wheel could drive a small hammer mill, in addition to a dynamo, it would be another asset. Tom the Harp had such a mill driven by his oil engine. It was rather like a big coffee-grinding machine, and he used it for grinding oats for his stock. It would conceivably make oatmeal for human consumption, and even flour, if fed with wheat.

I liked to think of these strictly utilitarian aspects of what we proposed to do, but I could not blind myself to the not so utilitarian aspects, especially the trout. With the warmer weather, these were now appearing in all the pools in the stream, none of them bigger than six inches, but in very great numbers. Those that were in the part of the stream which would be flooded would find their food supply enormously increased by the snails and larvae and fresh water shrimps feeding on the rotting vegetation. Those in the upper reaches of the stream would probably migrate to the lake, and if they didn't we could catch them with shrimping nets and transfer them.

The planning of the dam wall was my affair, with Clow to help in the actual construction, but before we actually closed it, the whole bed of the lake must be cleared of trees and bushes so that there would be no snags for fishing, boating or swimming, and in this job even the children willingly helped, especially as it meant making a bonfire out of the cleared material—a bonfire which, because of the blackout regulations, had to be put out before dark.

To make a permanent dam across a stream, you can't just build your wall across it. It would be like trying to repair a water main with the water full on. The stream must be temporarily diverted.

I had examined what was left of the original dam wall very carefully. It was built of the same slate slabs that had been used for the mansion. There was no mortar, but the slabs had been closely laid, and behind them was a great width of what I guessed was puddled clay. Under the old bed of the lake, which had been channelled by the stream, there was a thick deposit of clay. We could use this for packing the closing wall, which should consist of two walls of stone, eight feet apart at the foundations, decreasing to six at the top. It would have been better to pack with concrete. We had only two bags of cement, however, and I was reluctant to ask Eddy for more, as supplies were strictly rationed. The cost of concrete, too, made it prohibitive.

The first job was to clear the bed of the stream where it passed through the gap, and make a culvert. For the culvert, I had thought of using two forty-gallon oil drums, with their ends knocked out. End to end they'd make a tunnel six feet long and two feet in diameter. They would have to be embedded and packed all round with concrete, and for this I reckoned that our two bags of cement with eight of gravel and four of sand would do.

We had an argument about the culvert on our first Sunday. It would be much better, Clow said, to build it in the same way as the mansion drains, of slate slabs. There were plenty of these lying in the quarry, and they'd make a much neater job of it, and we shouldn't need to use more than a couple of buckets of cement mortar.

I pointed out that the virtue of having drums was that they made an arch, and that we'd need an arch to take the weight of the superimposed wall.

"*Jowl*, I could build an arch with the slabs, same as the breast of a chimney, and it would take the weight of a house."

"I know you could," I said, persuasively but firmly, "but it would take even you a long time, and we do want to get the thing finished as soon as we can, don't we? And we've only got Sundays to work on it. Let's stick to the drums. I'm certain they will do."

"Have it your own way, then," he grumbled, "but don't blame me if it doesn't work. You'll have to have a shutter for the culvert when the job's done. It's not going to be so easy to fit one over a round hole as it would be if it was square, and properly built. It's your own affair anyway."

It was, but I think he was admitting it reluctantly, and I was careful not to press home my moral victory.

"I hadn't thought of the shutter," I said. I had, but I thought the lie justified. "Couldn't you build a square entrance to the culvert hole, setting the first drum in a few inches from the face of the wall? A thick wood shutter would fit close up to it then."

He looked mollified.

"Now you're talking sense. I could make it so that the shutter would fit as tight as the cover on a jam pot. Let's get on with it and waste no more time."

Eager though I was to see the wall finished, the shutter closed against the stream, the water gradually rising and spreading over the lake bed, I knew that it was going to be a big job, and must not be hurried. Before we could set the drums, we had to divert the stream. Luckily there was little gravel where it ran through the gap. We found that its bed was solid slate, but soft enough to be dressed flat with a pick-axe. Clow cut a gulley on one side, deep enough to take the stream and leaving enough dry rock on the other side for the drums.

I made a temporary plank box, six feet long, three feet wide and nine inches deep, to rest on the rock, its length parallel to the course of the stream. We plugged its edges with clay, so that it would hold the liquid concrete. Clow mixed the first batch and shovelled it in to a depth of four inches. Then we set the drums in it on their sides, end to end, pressing them into the concrete, so that this rose slightly on each side, but not to the limits of the box depth. We wanted at least two inches of concrete between the drums and the solid rock.

I had some old corrugated iron sheets. We fixed these on edge so as to heighten the plank box by another two feet, and we shored them with stones and timber so that they would withstand the pressure of the concrete. The sheets fitted tightly at both orifices of the touching drums, but we left plenty of space at the sides. We filled the box with concrete, ramming in odd stones to eke out this precious material. Finally we had both drums encased.

We could remove the planks and the sheets when the concrete was set, in forty-eight hours. Then we could divert the stream from its temporary gulley into the culvert, fill the gulley with more concrete, and on this start building the permanent wall.

We had started work at eight o'clock. We'd had an hour's break for lunch, fifteen minutes for tea, and dusk was falling when the last bucket of concrete had been poured in. Clow had not once grumbled or made any criticism during the operation. I hadn't given him any orders, but I had explained at each phase what I wanted done, and he had done it, unquestioningly. Not that he had done all the hard work. I had helped to dig out the sand and gravel for the concrete. He had done the actual mixing, but I had carried most of it to the job, and although my enthusiasm remained, I wouldn't have been sorry to knock off for the day.

I hadn't reckoned with Clow's enthusiasm and energy. He didn't make any comment on the culvert. He looked at the gap on each side of it and he said:

"There's still an hour of daylight left, and I want to see this job done. We can't do anything at this until the concrete's set, but we're going to need a hell of a lot of stones to build up the wall, and then there's the pit for the wheel to build. We ought to have a big pile of stones ready for the job, and we ought to start getting them now."

I had of course told him what had happened when

we had visited the mill. His comment had been typical. He wanted all the credit.

"There you are. Didn't I tell you you'd get the wheel for nothing, or next to nothing? You wouldn't have gone unless I'd told you. It's no use to him, anyway. It would have meant work, if he'd had it going, and Dai's never done a day's work in his life—never dirtied his hands. Mind, he's a bit cracked. I don't know anything about poetry, but I'm told that what he writes is crazy. No one can make top nor tail of it."

"Not even the Welsh?"

"No, indeed."

More practically, Clow had confirmed that the iron part of the wheel was all right. It would be a simple matter to take it to bits, but it shouldn't be necessary to dismantle it completely. If we removed the top half of it, we could lift the lower half with a builder's tackle, and swing it on to the tractor trailer. He could drive the tractor close up to the dam wall and with the same gear lower it into our pit, when the pit was made.

"Have you made up your mind where you are going to fix the wheel?" Clow said now.

I was relieved to have his enthusiasm diverted from the stone gathering, but I didn't want him to show me where and how to fix the wheel. I had thought a great deal about it. I had carefully examined the ground below the wall, taken measurements, made drawings, and I was confident that I had got the right plan. As for the dam itself, I would need Clow's co-operation, but not his technical advice.

I said guardedly:

"Yes, I think I've got it roughly worked out. But I think we ought to finish the dam first, make certain that the level of water will be high enough. Don't you think we ought to pack up for the day, though?"

"Let's have a look below the wall first," he answered. We walked down through the gap, from which the stream fell steeply for some yards, making little cascades among the stones. From the standing part of the dam wall on the right side looking downstream, the bank of the stream was a cliff of earth and embedded stones, which I had myself surveyed. Clow pointed to it.

"Why—this is the very spot for the wheel. All we've got to do is to carve into the bank there, and make it straight, and build one wall against it, high enough to take the axle bearing of the wheel, and another wall opposite to take the other bearing. We're all right for height here. The top of the wheel will be about two feet lower than the lip of the dam wall. You'll need a sluice, of course. You can make that of timber, with a timber staging to hold it up. *Jowl*, it's as simple as ABC!"

I was crestfallen. Blast him, I thought, he might have been studying the plan I had so carefully drawn, which had even included timber trestles for the sluice. But I suppressed my anger.

"That's more or less what I planned," I said. "I'll have the sluice leading from about two feet below the dam spillway, with a sliding shutter to open and shut. But we can't settle about the wheel until the dam is finished."

I said this very firmly, and Clow answered:

"Just as you say. It's your affair. But I have a mind to get my pick and shovel and start squaring up that bank now. I want to see the whole job done. I want to see the wheel turning round."

I had to laugh.

"So do I," I said. "But it's getting late, and I'm tired, if you're not. Let's leave it till next Sunday."

He glanced reluctantly at the bank, and I could see that he was itching to begin work on it. But he turned and we moved back towards the gap and the boxed-in culvert. He stopped again as we reached it, and put one hand on the surface of the concrete.

"That will be hard set by Tuesday night," he said. "And there's a moon all this week. We needn't wait until Sunday. We can put in a couple of hours every night after I've finished on the fields, and get that wall built up. If you have any spare time during the day, you can be getting the stones for it. I've noticed there are plenty of them lying in the stream. And we'll need clay too. I want to see the job finished."

And then he actually paid me a compliment.

"It's not a bad idea, using those oil drums. It would have been better with a proper wall, but it's saved time. Don't make a heap of the stones when you get them. Spread them out near the job, so that I can see them and choose the ones I want. We ought to get the whole thing finished in a month."

14

MY CONSCIENCE was not completely clear about the building of the dam. Although Clow was putting in more than a full day's work at the fields, and I was doing the same with the fences and garden and other physical activities, it could have been argued that even our spare time and energy should have been devoted to strictly war-effort pursuits. Clow could have ploughed and harrowed by moonlight, and certainly on Sundays, for he had no religious scruples about Sunday work. I too could have done some of my gardening by the light of the moon, and I was only taking advantage of convention in regarding Sunday as a holiday.

Yet, apart from the two bags of cement that had gone for the culvert, we were not using any "war effort" material. The lake should produce a certain amount of food in the way of fish. The wheel should, by producing electricity, save paraffin and candles. If we got a mill, we might grind oatmeal, and if I could pick up a circular saw bench it might be used for sawing logs for the house fires, and save coal.

We removed the iron sheets from the culvert on the Tuesday evening, as dusk fell. The concrete was set like stone. We made a bank of clay to divert the stream from the gulley into the culvert, and by the time the moon rose we had filled the gulley with concrete, and Clow had begun the first course of stones, which he set in cement mortar for safety's sake. Above that it would be safe to use clay as mortar, for there would be the back wall too, with a space of eight feet between—a space that would be filled in with clay as the walls grew.

It was Clow's job again. I was his labourer. I kept him supplied with stones, some of them so big that I could just lift them. He worked at front and back walls alternately, and, as each course was built, I tipped a wheelbarrow load of wet clay in between them, and we trampled it down with our feet.

It was hard work. For once my job was harder than Clow's. I had to dig the clay from the stream bank about ten yards away from the wall, load it into the barrow, and wheel it along boards that we had laid on the soft ground. As the wall rose, the final board had to be slanted up, and as it was slippery with clay, it became increasingly difficult to keep the wheel in the middle of the board, and one's balance too—especially in the tricky light of the moon. Finally I had to abandon the wheelbarrow and resort to carrying the clay in buckets.

Hard and exhausting though it was, I felt that it was worthwhile. I had a constant vision before me of the finished wall, the water rising, the lake getting deeper and deeper, wider and wider, crystal clear like a sheet of glass, and I think that Clow was obsessed by the same vision.

Dain came down late that first evening, to see how we were getting on, and to tell me that supper was ready.

She laughed when she saw us, for at that moment we were both treading the wet clay, jumping up and down, and we must have made a fantastic sight in the moonlight—like savages engaged in a ritualistic dance.

"You've got on well," she said. "Won't it be exciting when it's all finished!"

"Yes, indeed, ma'am," Clow answered. "But Rome wasn't built in a day. *Jowl!* It's a pity we've got to leave off now, and only work on it evenings and Sundays. And there won't be any moon next week."

I knew he would have been quite willing to have gone on all night until the moon sank. I felt the same, but I knew that I had reached my physical limits. One more bucket of clay, and I would have dropped. We packed up, Clow politely refusing to come and have supper with us.

Although the temptation was strong, I religiously refrained from going even near the wall the next day. As the weather was propitious, we had started the sowing of the fields, and Clow needed my help with the drill. But we worked at it in the evening, and on every evening of the week, including Saturday. And as it was raining on Sunday, my conscience was doubly clear, for it would have been impossible to get on with the sowing.

The rain was continuous, yet not heavy. It made no appreciable difference to the volume of water in the stream. It was mild too, muggy, with mist on the hills. Good growing weather for grass, and the seeds sown in the fields and garden. The rain, if it eased my conscience, did not make our job any easier. Everything we touched, tools, bucket handles, stones, was wet and sticky and slippery with clay. We couldn't work in oilskins. They were too cumbersome. We just had to get wet. Clow did not seem to mind, however, and I certainly didn't, for steadily the wall was growing, bringing us nearer to the laying of the last stone, the exciting moment when we should fix the shutter on the culvert and watch the water start to rise.

As a wall increases in height, the materials with which it is built must be lifted higher. This made my own labour with the stones and clay more strenuous and difficult. How nice it would have been, I thought, if we'd had a mechanical grab, which would have dug into the clay, taking a great bite of it, then simply swung it over and deposited it on the wall; or a crane to lift some of the heavier stones (so heavy that Clow had to come down and help me when I got to the bottom of the wall) and swing them into position.

It all had to be done by hand, in the most difficult way. Yet, as the wall grew higher, it also grew narrower. It was vertical in the front, the lake side, but on the back, each course of stones was set a little nearer in, making a slope in the best tradition of dams.

The wall, indeed, was almost half-finished when we knocked off at dusk. There was no temptation to wait for the moon, for it was still raining, and the sky was completely overcast.

"*Jowl*," Clow said, as he swung the wet haversack that contained his bait tin over his shoulders, and looked at the last course of stones. "I'm wet through to the bloody skin, but it's going well. I've never built a dam wall before, but I'm damned if anyone could have done it better. You'll not get a drop of water leaking through that. If it wasn't for the sowing, we could get the whole thing finished by the end of next week. We can't touch the fields if it goes on raining like this."

Was he praying that it would?

It wasn't raining next morning, but it was drizzling and overcast, with no wind or sun to dry the soil. With clear consciences we worked at the dam wall. Tuesday, Wednesday, Thursday, brought no appreciable change in the weather. By this time the soil had got so wet that we should need at least two days of continuous dry weather to get it into condition. We carried on with the wall.

There was a clear dawn on Friday, and a strong, cold easterly wind. If it lasted all day and all Saturday, then on Sunday we must leave the wall for the fields, no matter how near we were to finishing it. It rained again on Friday night, however. It was raining on Saturday morning when we started to lay the last course of stones and make the spillway. Then, early in the afternoon, it stopped raining. The sky cleared, the sun came out, the warm spring sun. And the wall was finished.

We'd had lunch. Most of the children had been down watching Clow doing the finishing touches. There only remained an occasion—an occasion which to me was as exciting and dramatic as the launching of a ship: the closing of the culvert. I wanted everyone, including our friends, to be present.

Although there was no school, Jane had ridden into Castlebridge to tell them at the Jew's Harp, and to ask them if they would telephone to Eddy, for I had promised that I would let him know. We had sent a message by Albert the Post to Dai the Mill, inviting him to come.

Eddy was the first of our friends to arrive. Clow gave a baleful glance at him as he approached.

"We'll soon know if there's anything wrong with the job," he growled. "I've no doubt he'll think he could have done it better himself. You'd better tell him it was not my idea using those drums for the culvert."

To my relief, Eddy was anything but critical.

"Man!" he said—and I was glad he said "man" and that he was looking at Clow when he spoke. "You've made a fine job of it. It looks strong enough to hold the flood itself. And you've got all the ground nicely cleared. My! It's going to be a big lake. It's going to look beautiful—beautiful! But it's a pity you haven't got the water-wheel yet."

Clow looked pleased. "I'll have that fixed in good time," he said modestly. "That wall's not going to leak. I could have done it better if I'd had more time. It's been a rush job. The culvert should have been stone. It all ought to have been concrete by rights, but I've had to use cement as though it was as scarce as butter."

We hadn't made the wall completely continuous with the old wall of the dam. We had left a gap, eight feet wide and two feet deep, to take the actual stream (allowing for spate) when the lake was full, and Clow's last job had been to pave this with slates embedded in cement. There was a gap, too, four feet wide and four feet deep for the waterwheel sluice. I had made a frame for this with angle iron, to take an adjustable wooden shutter.

Clow had carefully squared up the orifice of the culvert. We had found a slab of slate in the quarry, four inches thick, that would fit over the orifice when the time came. As an extra precaution, I had glued a thickness of roofing felt on to the face of the slab, to act like the gasket between the block and cylinder head of a water-cooled engine.

The slab was standing close to the orifice. I could not lift it myself, but I was determined that my hands would at least be on it when it was moved into position, and that would be as soon as the family and our invited friends assembled.

They now came crowding down: Porgy and Parkey and the smaller children, and Dain with Amy and Sara and Tom and Mano, with several of Mano's own village scholars. Then came Albert the Post on his way back from his rounds. Dai couldn't come, he told us. He was working on a poem, and he couldn't spare the time—but he would come and look at the lake one day. Perhaps he would write a poem about it!

Mother wasn't able to come either, Amy told me. She'd got a touch of rheumatics, and was sitting by the fire with Nellie to keep her company. I was relieved in a way. She had a sharp tongue. She could never disguise her dislike of Clow, and I didn't want the occasion spoilt by any unpleasantness. I was a little afraid of Amy putting her foot into it by giving me too much credit for what I'd done, and discounting Clow's contribution. I should have liked to explain to her that he had done all his work for nothing, and that in the actual building of the wall I had been only the unskilled labourer.

Clow, however, held himself aloof from all our visitors. He had jumped down the wall, and was standing near the culvert orifice. I was still on the wall top.

"Are we all ready now?" he shouted to me. "There's no need for you to come down. I can manage the slab by myself."

I had a shock. He had already got his hands on the slab.

"No!" I shouted vehemently. "We're not ready yet. Wait!"

I jumped down on the opposite side of the culvert. I didn't want to show him what a fright he'd given me—that I would have been furious if he had done the thing by himself. I said, as calmly as I could:

"We must do it together. I'll give you a hand with it. I think we're ready now."

"All right. But watch out. There's a force in the stream. It will flood back as soon as it's shut."

The stream, although not in spate, had increased in volume since we had first diverted it into the culvert. It was more than halfway up the diameter of the drums, and running with considerable velocity. I don't think that Clow could have done the job single-handed. Certainly I could not have done it alone.

"Get hold of it now," Clow ordered. "We'll keep it flat at first, then slant it against the stream, and lower it slanting on to the sill. When it's there, we'll raise it and let the stream itself shut it."

I was no longer feeling angry with him. Probably

he'd only been actuated by unselfish motives in offering to do the thing alone. He could not have guessed how significant it was to me. But I was trembling with excitement. The moment had come.

The slab was leaning against the wall. He moved it, still upright, to the edge of the stream, and leaning across I got a purchase of it with both hands. We lifted it, flat, and moved it until we were about a foot away from the culvert.

"Slant it now," Clow ordered, "and keep it slanted."

Its bottom edge touched the water, and I could feel the power of the stream against it.

"Lower it. Lower."

We lowered it. The water swirled above our arms. The slab felt as light as wood, as if it were floating.

"Lower, lower!" Clow shouted. "It's got to be on the sill and dead centre. There it is. It's touching. Hold on, now. A bit this way. It's centre now. Keep your fingers out of the way. Right, let it come up."

I hung on until the last moment, as the slab, with the force of the stream behind it, rose to the vertical, and closed with a thud on the frame of the culvert. Instantly the stream lost its velocity, and began to swirl around us, and it was over our gumboot tops before we could get out of the way. There was laughter and excited shouts from the children, and a shout from Clow:

"Some of you look the other side of the wall. See if there's any water coming through the culvert."

It was Eddy who looked.

"Man," he shouted, "the stream's gone. Not a drop of water coming through. Why, there's some little trout there, high and dry."

There were more excited shouts from the children. I climbed up the wall to see Amelia and Macky, each with a live fish in their hands, Angus and Christine trying to catch another.

"Bring them this side of the wall," I cried, "and let them go into the lake. Don't hurt them."

Curiously, it had never entered my head that our damming of the stream would be so successful as to dry it out below. Fortunately, there were plenty of pools between the dam and the quarry, and below the quarry there was a small tributary stream, and there should be few casualties among the fish population. The children ran up with their captives, and dropped them into the water, and for the time being their interest, like my own, was engaged by what was happening on the lake side of the wall.

It was profoundly exciting. Already the water was well above the top edge of the culvert slab. There was a deep winding gulley in the old bed of the lake. Before we had shut the culvert, the stream itself, spreading across the width of this gulley, had been shallow. One could have crossed it anywhere without wetting more than the soles of one's boots. Now the gulley was filling. Near the wall it had reached the edge on both sides and was creeping over the level bed which we had cleared. One could have rowed a dinghy up the gulley for at least twenty yards.

We were all, except Albert, who had remembered his official duties, crowding on the dam wall now. Dain, with Timothy by my side, Amelia, Jane and Angus nearby. All of us watching the water rise.

"Look!" Amelia cried. "It's just like the tide coming in. Isn't it lovely! Will it be long before it gets to the top of the wall? Oh, I do wish we had a boat."

"Will you make a boat, Daddy?" Angus asked anxiously.

"Oh, do, *do*!" Jane joined in, and Timothy said: "I want a boat, Daddy."

"See what you've let yourself in for," Eddy laughed. "You'll have to make them a boat. But what I want to see now is your waterwheel working."

"I'll have that fixed as soon as he's decided where he wants it to go," put in Clow. "It had to be the wall first. I've never built a dam wall before, but there's not much wrong with it, is there?" And, answering Amelia's question: "It'll take a day or two to fill, but I guarantee it will fill all right."

Dear Clow, I thought, he couldn't help swanking, taking complete credit for it. I was glad that Amy was out of hearing, for I knew that she shared her mother's dislike for him, and she might have been tempted to try and deflate his conceit. She, Sara, Tom and Mano were all watching the rising water as though entranced. Suddenly Amelia cried:

"Let's see if there are any more trout below the dam. Let's take a bucket and bring them to the lake."

There were wild whoops from the other children, and away they went.

Dain squeezed my hand.

"It's exciting, isn't it? It's going to be almost as good as the real sea. I think you've made a wonderful job of it."

204

Clow didn't hear that. No, I didn't mind his swanking. He could call it Clow's dam if he liked. With his help (and I could not have done without it) I had got something I had wanted ever since I poached my first trout in my native Miller's Dam. I was full of warmth towards him.

15

THE LAKE was better than anything I had imagined or hoped for. It was as lovely to look at as our beloved Cornish creek, to which, in many ways, it had a nostalgic resemblance. That creek, as seen from the front windows of our wooden hut, was framed with high banks, which protected it from all but the strongest winds. The banks were brackeny, with a few oak trees, clumps of gorse, and outcrops of grey, lichen-covered rocks. There were no other houses in sight, for the creek curved from left to right, away from our cove.

The creek was tidal, of course. At low water, what we saw from the house was a stretch of level mud between the opposing banks, with a narrow ribbon of hard shingle beach. The mud itself had a special fascination, for it was foraging ground for innumerable wading birds—gulls, curlews, oyster-catchers, red-shanks, sandpipers and herons. At high tide, in fine weather, the creek would be like a mirror in which the banks would be reflected—a mirror whose polished surface would be wrinkled by a cruising swan, or perhaps by a leaping salmon, or, more exciting still, by a shoal of grey mullet, which, on lucky days, would venture into our cove so that we could get a trammel net round them. And the view would be completed by the sight of our motor boat, riding at its mooring just outside the cove, reflected in the water, and by our dinghy drawn up on the beach.

Our lake bore no comparison with the creek in size. From the dam wall to its tapered end, where the stream entered, it measured a hundred yards, and at its greatest width it was scarcely fifty. Yet its banks on the side opposite the meadow were almost identical in shape and composition with those of the creek. There was bracken, gorse, stunted oaks, outcrops of grey rock, and these banks, as in the creek, were reflected in the polished surface of the water.

The water itself was crystal clear. Standing on the dam wall, or at any point along the shores, one could see every detail of the bottom. There was no tide to rise and fall. It was perpetual high water. There were, at first, no water birds, no leaping salmon or shoals of mullet. But there were trout, scores of them, some that the children had caught below the dam when the stream had temporarily dried, some which had been in the pools of the stream where it had coursed through the gulley, but more, which I guessed were migrating downstream, where they instinctively realised the existence of a better feeding ground.

We could see them feeding among the drowned

vegetation on the lake bed. Better still, we could see them rising to fly as the spring advanced and the weather grew warmer. I had no temptation to fish for them. The biggest were still no bigger than six inches. They must grow and they must breed, but in fairness I could not forbid the elder children to fish, although I made it a rule that any trout under six inches must be put back.

I knew it was not a generous gesture on my part. Indeed, it was rather cunning. Trout are among the wariest and most fastidious of all fish. Small earth worms, the standard bait for them, do not live under water. They only become available in rainy weather when streams are swollen and scour earth from their banks. This process also muddies the water, helping to make the angler's hook and line invisible.

Trout do not expect to see earth worms when streams or lakes are low and clear. If one, unattached to hook and line, does drop within their sight, and the very plop of it hasn't frightened them, they will examine it very suspiciously, and nine times out of ten will leave it alone. It looks fishy. If the worm is impaled on a hook, attached even to the finest of lines, then it would be a most unusual trout that would swallow it and allow itself to be caught.

I was pretty certain that the trout in the lake were safe, that the only way to catch them would be with fly, using the finest of tackle, a fly rod, and a technique most difficult to acquire—impossibly so for a child. I did not encourage the children to fish. I did not discourage them. Amelia, Jane, Angus and Macky pestered me for gear. I gave them snooded trout hooks, lines, and told them to cut hazel wands for rods—the apparatus with which I had caught my first trout in the Miller's Dam, the water in which, however, had been muddy on that occasion. I showed them a plot in the garden which would benefit by some more forking, and showed them how to obtain suitable worms, doing the forking themselves—killing two birds with one stone. I warned them that fishing called for patience, and they mustn't expect to catch such fish as trout simply by throwing the baited hook into the water. They must be quiet and never let the fish see them; and I felt that I had done my duty, both to the children and to the fish. I had learned my fishing the hard way. So must they.

They fished in the evenings when they got back from school, and on Saturdays and Sundays. They were, as I had guessed, unsuccessful, and very soon Amelia, Jane and Angus gave it up. The trout simply wouldn't look at their bait. They found it more exciting to fish in the stream itself above and below the dam, catching the trout with their bare hands, putting them in a bucket and bringing them down to the lake. But Makubwa was not discouraged. He had the instincts and temperament of the real fisherman. Nothing except a stern call to meals or bed would get him away from the lake.

He had selected and cut his hazel rod with great care, and dressed all the roughness off with his pocket knife. It was long, thin, whippy. As he had no reel, he had taken the wise precaution of winding the line down the rod from tip to butt. He did not try to fish from the wall, but chose the far bank where he could hide among the bushes at the water's edge. He deserved success.

One Saturday afternoon I saw him there, and as I had been working hard, I was tempted to take a spell of rest and watch him. I had built a wooden bridge across the spillway of the dam. I crossed it, and made my way among the brambles and gorse to the point immediately above the place, where, near the water's edge and close by the ivy-covered stump of an oak, he was standing.

I had moved very quietly so as not to frighten the fish from his neighbourhood, and I do not think he was aware of my presence. He was completely absorbed.

The water near the bank was about six feet deep. There was no wind. As usual, the water was clear. Conditions could not have been more unfavourable for worm fishing. A few feet away from the shore were several trout, all about five inches in length. The children had caught dozens of this size by hand in the stream, and brought them to the lake. They were not, apparently, feeding. They were at half depth, swimming very slowly round and round as though they had been in an aquarium. And just as clearly as I could see the fish, I could see Makubwa's bait, moving very slowly, in obedience to the movement of his rod tip.

He was, I could see, deliberately putting the bait ahead of a swimming fish so that it couldn't help seeing it, and, if it carried on its course, touching it. Within an inch or two of the bait, however, the fish did alter course, not nervously, as though frightened by the bait or the line, but as though the worm just didn't interest it in any way. Not discouraged, Makubwa gently moved the bait into the track of another fish.

I knew it was hopeless. Not for anything would I

have told him so, however. He was happy. He was experiencing the true joy of angling, which is not just catching fish, but pitting your own wits against theirs. How I wished and prayed, though, that his patience and skill would be rewarded, that one of those trout would have its foolish moment, swallow the bait and be caught.

And then the unexpected happened, as it so often does in fishing.

A few yards farther out than the trout was a boulder, in the original gully of the stream. From under this there appeared a large eel, swimming along the bottom and in the direction of the shore. It was the largest eel I had ever seen in fresh water. It was well over a yard in length, and for an eel it had a very thick body. From my own vantage point I could see its little beady eyes, its whitish lips, and its mouth open to seize something—possibly a snail or grub.

Had Makubwa seen it? I dared not shout for fear of frightening the fish. His bait was still dangling in the water near the trout. The eel was soon not more than eight feet away from him, still coming his way. Surely he had seen it now? If he did, surely he didn't expect the eel to see his bait and swim up from the bottom?

I was underestimating Makubwa's intelligence and skill. He had seen it. He was still crouching among the sheltering ivy. I saw him stiffen a little and then slowly raise the tip of his rod, until the bait was clear of the water. He raised the rod to the vertical, and took the bait in his hand. Then he let go, gave a flick of the rod, and sent the bait outwards in the direction of the eel—and with a hazel rod I certainly could not have done it better myself.

The bait hit the water with a gentle plop. It began to sink, and it reached the bottom not more than six inches in front of the eel's snout. There was no hesitation on the eel's part. It saw the bait, opened its mouth and closed it again, still swimming on. I saw the line tauten. Makubwa gave a quick jerk to it. The eel made a lightning spurt as it felt the prick of the hook, and the next moment the rod was bent like a bow as Makubwa, with both hands on the butt, swung it ashore.

I could not have been more thrilled if it had been a ten-pound salmon and I had landed it myself. He had got both hands on it when I reached him, its slimy tail coiled round one arm. I helped him to kill it and remove the hook.

I patted him on the back .

"Bravo, bravo!" I cried. "Take it up to the house and show it to the other children."

He grinned and said politely, but firmly:

"Beg pardon. Not yet, if you don't mind. I want to catch another first." And, like a true fisherman. he baited his hook again.

Clow wanted to get on with the installation of the water-wheel straight away, and he offered to work at the building of the pit every evening, and on Sundays, and on moonlit nights.

Although I wanted to do it so much myself, my conscience forbade. Now that the evenings were getting longer, the children were going to bed in daylight. The matter of illumination was not so urgent, and I could hardly justify the time we would spend on the wheel, on patriotic grounds. I hadn't acquired a dynamo yet, although Eddy had promised to look out for a second-hand one, and for the wiring and fittings we should need for an electric installation, none of which we would be permitted to buy new.

The farm, the garden, must now take complete priority of our time and energy. The children were pestering me to start building a boat. Again there was nothing I would have liked to do more. Again it would have to be deferred.

The war news continued to be very grim. Although there was comfort in the fact that the Yanks were "in it" they had not been able to stem the Japanese tide of invasion, nor had our forces in the Far East been able to do much to help. The Japs were holding the Dutch East Indies. They had landed in New Guinea. Their aircraft had dropped bombs on the mainland of Australia, and Australian troops had been transferred from the Middle East, where they were badly needed, for the defence of their own country, now under threat of invasion.

In North Africa, Rommel was preparing for a final assault in Egypt and the Suez Canal. Although the Russians were fighting hard, it looked as though they would be unable to stop the Nazis' easterly and southerly advance unless the Allies created a second front in the West by the invasion of the European mainland.

The Royal Air Force was still bearing the brunt, offensive and defensive, of the air war in the West. The Yanks with their Flying Fortresses were coming, but they hadn't come yet. British sea ports and cities were still being raided. Nazi, and even Italian war plants, were being heavily bombed.

The British Navy was still bearing the brunt of the Battle of the Atlantic, protecting our own shipping lanes and those to the Arctic ports of Russia, from surface, underwater and air attack. The U-boat offensive had only been partly diverted to the Western Atlantic and the seaboard of America, tying up most of the American Atlantic fleet with convoy protection. Our losses, in sailors' lives, in ships and cargoes of munitions and oil and food, continued to be heavy.

We must grow more food, produce more milk, meat, eggs, vegetables, and go on producing them. I must put the waterwheel out of my mind at least until we had finished all operations on the land and garden. I had been able to do little to help with the sowing of the oats. Clow wouldn't let me drive the tractor. If he had done, it would have meant that he would have been idle, for our vegetable garden was not in the partnership. I had plenty to do, however, when it came to the planting of the potatoes.

I had already sown a big patch of early potatoes in the garden, and that in itself had been a stiff job. We had four acres of potatoes to sow, and although the tractor could, using a special single plough, make the furrows, bury the *sets*, each set had to be laid by hand at intervals of a foot.

The furrows were a yard apart. A square acre measures roughly seventy yards by seventy, so that there were seventy furrows to each acre, each seventy yards in length—a total of about four thousand nine hundred linear yards, about two and one quarter miles for one acre, *nine* miles for the four!

There were tractor-drawn potato drills which would do sowing and burying in one operation. They were very expensive, and the committee told us there wasn't one available for hire. They were all needed for bigger farms.

It was a long, wearisome, back-breaking job. Clow had already ploughed and disc-harrowed the field, which, when we had started, had been almost entirely grown over with bracken. He had ploughed deep to get at the matted roots of these, but I doubted if he had killed them. The field had received only a light dressing of ground limestone, for lime was supposed to encourage scab in potatoes. I knew, from my gardening experience, that the best fertiliser for potatoes is stable manure, spread thickly in the furrows and the sets dropped into it, and then covered with soil. No stable manure was available. We were obliged to use an artificial manure, a small handful with each set—another operation.

No wonder the Government was paying £10 subsidy for each acre of potato sown!

We offloaded the sacks of sets and bags of fertiliser from the trailer at convenient intervals on the field. When Clow had ploughed a furrow, we would start at opposite ends of it, first dropping the sets from buckets filled at the nearest sack. When we met, we'd turn back and sow the fertiliser, and when this was done Clow would plough the next furrow, the soil from which would bury the first.

Nine miles! It took us three weeks, and when it was

done, it was still only half of an eight-acre field whose boundaries one could walk round in a matter of minutes. And if all went well, each of the sets we had sown would produce at least eight potatoes, each one of which would have to be lifted by hand, dropped in a bucket, which would be emptied in a sack, which in turn would have to be lifted on to the dray, and off-loaded again to be sorted and made into a clamp, or otherwise stored until the crop was sold.

Our potato harvest was a long way off, however. Clow didn't need my help for the sowing of the other four acres of that field with mangolds and swedes. There was another job for me. The oats he had sown were coming on very nicely. But for twenty blades of oats there was at least one thistle, which, invigorated by the fertilisers, looked like emulating Jack's famous beanstalk. I couldn't hoe them all. To get round the whole thirty acres would have taken months. I just went for the biggest of them, hoping that in the struggle for existence, the oats would beat the smaller ones, and choke them.

There was no time for the waterwheel or a boat. The garden itself was almost a full-time job, although with this Dain and Porgy and the children helped, especially with the weeding. We had long rows of broad beans, peas and runners. The peas and runners had to be staked. The stakes had to be cut and carried from the wood. We had beds of lettuces, carrots, rows of cabbages and broccoli. We'd planted gooseberry, blackcurrant, logans for next year, and a strawberry bed which we hoped would fruit this. We'd hopefully put in some open-air tomato plants too, and vegetable marrows.

Would we make money out of the garden? Judging by the rate at which the first lettuces were consumed by our own household, I felt doubtful. Still, as Dain pointed out, if we'd had to buy these from the shops, we'd have had to pay a terrific price for them, and they were so much nicer than shop ones, anyway. It would be the same with our peas and early potatoes.

It was no good worrying. We were producing food if we were not producing money. It was a joy to see how the garden flourished as the summer drew on, to see the oat fields, despite the thistles, turning to an almost uniform green; to see the first potato leaves shooting from the soil (albeit with more thistles), and to see the wind waving in the almost luxuriant grass of the home meadow.

I'd had my first dip in the lake, diving in from the dam wall. The water was cold, and it lacked the tang and buoyancy of salt water. Yet it was good, and those of the children who could swim were soon having their daily dip, with an adult always in attendance, and the other children were as happy at the shallow end, with its sand and shingle.

We had been buying all our seed and fertilisers from Eddy, and he had remained a regular and very welcome visitor. It was on a warm sunny day in June, and we were at lunch when we heard the sound of a car coming along the drive from the front gate. Amelia jumped up and looked through the window.

"It's Eddy, and he's got a trailer with something big on it "—and her voice became an ecstatic shout.

"It's a boat! It's a boat!"

It *was* a boat—a stout, broad-beamed, fourteen-foot dinghy.

Eddy was quite apologetic.

"I hope you don't mind my doing this," he said to me. "I know you would rather have got one yourself, or built one, but it wouldn't have been easy, would it? And I knew how much the children wanted one. It's only a loan, anyhow. It belongs to a friend of mine down on the coast. As you know, no one's allowed to use small boats there because of the defence regulations. I had to get a permit from the police even to bring it here, and you've got to promise not to leave the oars and rowlocks in after dark!"

Such indeed were the regulations that had been made after the Nazi armies had swept into the Netherlands, and we had first heard the phrase "Fifth Columnist". All privately-owned craft along the British coasts must be immobilised, in case they should be of use to the expected invaders or their agents.

There was no need for me to assure Eddy that I did not resent his action. He had drawn up outside the front door. We were all crowding round him and the trailer, the children looking at the boat with rapt excitement.

"I'm in a hurry," Eddy went on. "I've got a lot of calls to make this afternoon, but I'd like to see the boat afloat first. Shall we get it in straight away? Can I get the car down to the lake without damaging your grass? My, but the meadow is looking good. You'll have to be cutting it soon. You're going to get a good crop."

I had fenced a broad path through the meadow to the garden and the dam wall, which I had kept close-cropped with a scythe. It was the children's cricket pitch. Eddy backed the car and trailer down it until the trailer was close to the wall. Then we got out of his car, and we started to undo the lashings of the dinghy.

For safety's sake, I had made a wire-netting fence this side of the lake, extending to the bridge over the spillway. It didn't take me long to remove a section of it wide enough to allow the dinghy through. There was a drop of only a foot to the surface of the water. We lowered the dinghy from the trailer to the ground, everyone helping, or trying to help.

To me, there was nothing so exciting as a boat. The very smell of it, and it had a faint tang of the sea, was like wine to me. It was beautiful, too, clinker built of American pine, varnished, copper fastened, all her metal fittings, including the rowlocks, solid brass.

I was sure that Eddy would not resent my now taking charge of the operation. I lifted up the stern sheet, made sure that the plug was in.

"Who's going in her?" I asked. "Who's going to pull? It won't hold everyone. You'll have to take turns."

There were excited shouts. It seemed that all the children wanted to go in her, and that all of them, including Timothy, who had never been in a boat, wanted to pull.

"I think that Mr Jones should be the one to pull," I said.

Eddy laughed.

"No, I couldn't pull a boat. Besides, I might be seasick." He looked at Dain. "Ladies first, anyway."

"Come on then, let's launch her."

We all got hold and we pushed her stern first over the edge of the wall. A final push and she was afloat, and I couldn't have been more excited if I had built her myself and it was her first launching. I was itching to jump in and take the sculls for one quick pull round the lake. I resisted the temptation.

"You get in first," I said to Dain.

She got in, and expertly unshipped the sculls.

"It's just like Cornwall, isn't it?" she cried to me.

I was thinking the same thing. But for the crowd of children, it might have been our Cornish creek on another such lovely summer's day, with us setting off on a fishing expedition.

"Who's next?" I said. "You can't all get in. You've got to take turns."

Amelia, who could pull a boat, nobly stood down for Christine and the Southampton evacuees. So did Mary and Jane, but Ellen got in. Makubwa, whose manners were always perfect, also stood aside. The twins, standing as usual hand in hand, didn't look eager anyway, but I saw no reason why Angus and Timothy shouldn't be amongst the first passengers. With eight on board, including Dain, I pushed off, and away they went across the lake, Dain pulling as though she had never lost a day's practice since our happy days in Cornwall. Those of us on shore cheered.

I turned to Eddy and shook his hand.

"You know, it's wonderful of you to have done this for us. You've no idea what it means to us to have a boat again. You've been wonderful to us from the start. And to think that it all happened just because you came to the station that night to meet a friend who didn't turn up."

He laughed.

"On my birthday, too! Man, the pleasure's mine. It's a good thing to make little ones happy, anyhow. It's always a pleasure for me to come out here. My—the lake's beautiful. Beautiful! And with the boat on it, too. But what about the waterwheel? I want to see that going. And, by the way, a piece of luck. The man who owns that boat—he's a bus proprietor, by the way—has got a twenty-five volt dynamo and batteries, and any amount of old electric cable. In bits and pieces, but with a low voltage, it would be safe enough just joining it up and using insulating tape. You could have it all for a song. Shall I bring it out to you next time I come?"

I laughed.

"Eddy *bach*, you're the devil! You tempted me about the lake the first time you came out. Now you're tempting me about the wheel. Of course I want to see it going. But there are so many things to do first. I ought to be up on the potato field now, pulling out thistles. And, as you say, the meadow's ready to be mown. But I would like to see that dynamo, and the cable. Thank you again, Eddy *bach*."

16

FOR SECURITY reasons, there were no weather forecasts on the radio, but it seemed that the fine weather would last, and in the first week in July Clow decided to make a start on the meadow.

We had hired a mowing-machine from the committee. Although I had often watched a mower at work, and had helped in most other operations connected with haymaking, I had never handled the machine itself. The shaft of this was bolted on to the draw bar of the tractor. It moved on a pair of iron wheels, which, like the wheels of a lawnmower, worked the cutting blades, but these, instead of rotating, were horizontal, shaped like sharks' teeth, with a scissor-like action. The cutter extended at right angles from the lower part of the machine, and was lowered to or raised from ground level by a lever.

The lever was controlled from the driver's seat, not from the tractor. The operation of mowing therefore required two men. I had to drive the mower. It was, Clow explained, simple enough. All I had to do was lower the cutter, raise it when we came to the end of a swath and had to make a turn, or when it was choked, as it would be at times, when we'd have to stop and clear it.

The seat was made of iron, moulded more or less to the shape of a man's backside. It was supported by a rigid iron bar rising from the chassis of the machine. There were foot rests, like those on a motorbike, but nothing to hang on to with one's hands except the lever and the edge of the seat itself.

There was no padding to the seat. Those who had designed it must have thought that all farmers were well fed and endowed with a natural padding, or a very insensitive nervous system. I had neither, and as the weather was so warm I was wearing light drill shorts. But I hadn't guessed yet what I was in for.

We made a start at the end of the meadow, nearest the main gate, and from this point I assumed that we would make a circuit of the whole field, which was rectangular in shape, with the stream making one long side, the road (and the mansion and farm buildings) the other. Our first drive was along one of the shorter sides toward the road, which happened to be uphill.

Clow started on low gear. He gave me a shout. I dropped the cutter lever, and I saw the grass falling behind it in a clean swath. We carried on, still uphill, still in low gear. We approached the boundary fence, and Clow shouted:

"Right. Up she comes!"

I pulled the lever. The cutter rose. Clow stopped, and leaving the engine running, got down from his own more comfortable seat.

He looked at the swath we had cut, about fifty yards in length, six feet wide.

"Very nice," he said. "We'll be on the level now for a

bit, and be able to go quicker. Let's get the corner cleared."

So far, although the seat was uncomfortably hard, there had been little to distress me, and I'd been completely concentrated on the job. Clow had a hay fork in the tractor. He quickly cleared the cut grass from the end of the swath, to enable him to turn, and the cutter to bite into the virgin grass.

He backed and turned. We were now facing the mansion, about two hundred yards away. He started. I dropped the lever, and then, without any warning, he put the tractor into top gear, and if I hadn't been grasping the lever, I'd have been bumped out of my seat.

It wasn't just the sudden acceleration that did it, however, for the bumping went on. I had imagined that the surface of the field was smooth. For walking over, it was. But the flat iron wheels had to follow every irregularity of the ground-hillocks, ant heaps, mole hills, odd stones, which, when walking, one would not have noticed. There were no springs to absorb the shock, which was transmitted and amplified to that iron seat, compared with which the bony back of a runaway mule would have been like a foam rubber mattress.

I hung on to the lever with one hand, the edge of the seat with the other. We got almost to the kitchen window, then Clow shouted again. I raised the lever, and he stopped. Dain was at the window, smiling.

"It does look good," she cried. "It's so thick, isn't it? It's going to be a lovely crop."

I was smiling myself, as I got down and walked up to her, but a little grimly, and I was rubbing my bruised backside. Clow was again busy clearing the grass for the next swath.

"Darling," I said, "could you pass me one of the chair cushions. The thicker the better."

The cushion did make a difference, but not much, for, apart from the bumping, there was a constant vibration which I could feel even when we stopped to make our turns, as a sailor feels the roll of a ship when he walks on level ground. The next swath took us past the mansion. Then we turned at full speed up the longer side of the field to the boundary corner. We came hell for leather down to the stream boundary then, and passing the garden had an almost straight run to the end of the field from where we had started. And, as we passed the garden and the lake, I breathed a prayer of thankfulness that I had made the garden so big, that there was so much less of the meadow to be mown.

By this time I had bumped the cushion as hard as a board. I felt that I was being beaten on the backside with a rope end. All my limbs were dithering with the vibration. Yet I was determined not to let Clow see what discomfort I was suffering, to have him think I couldn't take it. Besides, there was a thrill in what we were doing, in seeing the long swaths of cut grass, already starting to wilt in the hot sunshine and yield a suspicion of the delicious perfume of real hay.

And gradually, as one gets used to most forms of pain and discomfort when they are inevitable, I got used, or at least inured to that infernal machine. I was glad when we came to the uphill sections and we had to travel in low gear. I was glad when occasionally the cutter got choked, and we both had to dismount and spend quite a time clearing it. I would have been happier if Clow hadn't driven at such speed downhill and on the level. By watching the tractor, however, I learnt to anticipate the worst of the bumps and to pull myself up from the seat as they came, like rising in the saddle of a trotting horse.

I was glad, of course, when lunchtime came, which gave me the opportunity for changing my drill shorts for riding breeches, and getting another cushion. But I was almost as glad when the time came to start again. By then we had cut nearly a quarter of the field. The sun was blazing. The smell was becoming more definitely that of hay.

It was double summer time. We had started work at eight o'clock, giving the dew a chance to dry. We had half-an-hour's break at tea. We carried on, with the sun still shining, until seven o'clock, when we knocked off for supper. It was still shining when we started again at eight o'clock, and there remained about two acres to do in the middle of the meadow, with a final sweep round the boundaries to take what we'd missed at the first cut.

I was, to a certain extent, refreshed by the meal. I was so stiff and sore, however, that I winced with the effort of climbing on to the torture seat. We started on the remaining pitch, round and round, stopping at each corner to clear the swath. The grass was thicker here, and the ground was even bumpier. Time after time the cutter choked and we had to clear it. Yet Clow did not reduce speed. I was so weary soon that I couldn't raise myself to the bumps. I just endured them.

The sun sank. We carried on. And at last the patch

was reduced to a single strip, the width of the cutter. We took it at one sweep, and then, without stopping, Clow drove on to the point where we had started, near the gate, and we began the final sweep of the verges, in the reverse direction. We had to make a complete circuit of the field. In ten minutes we were back at the gate again. I pulled the lever for the last time. Clow stopped the engine. The job was done.

I felt no immediate joy. I had the feeling that I was waking from an unpleasant dream. Although the engine had stopped, I could still hear the noise of it. Although the mowing machine was still, I could still feel the vibration of the lever, the brutal bumping of the seat on which I was still sitting. Then Clow spoke.

"So that job's done. *Jowl*—we've got a good crop too. Better than I thought. A week of this weather and we'll have it in the yard. I told you that you'd find it easy working the mowing-machine. There's nothing like a tractor and modern machinery. It would have taken two days to cut this field with a horse. I'd like to get my meadow mown tomorrow—only four acres. Perhaps you'd come and give me a hand?"

Clearly, Clow was happy, not a bit tired, still full of beans. I climbed wearily, painfully, down from my seat to the ground, and with an effort held myself upright.

"Of course I'll give you a hand," I said, and I dared to swank: "What a pity the light's gone, or we could have started straight away."

Thank heaven, I thought, that it was nearly dark.

17

HAY MAKING, in a district of relatively small farms or holdings, must of necessity be a communal operation. A farmer can do his own mowing with a minimum of help. With a tractor and modern implements (or with a horse, for that matter, but the job takes longer) he can turn the swaths over to let the air and sun get at the under part of them, and when the crop is really dry he can rake it mechanically into long windrows, which can then be raked into convenient sized heaps ready for leading. If the weather is threatening, and leading not practical, these heaps can be made into cocks, or miniature stacks, which will withstand a fair amount of rain, although when a dry spell comes they will have to be broken up and re-dried.

It is in the leading and stacking that extra help is needed. On big, completely mechanised farms, the stacking is facilitated by powered loaders, which are really conveyor belts, and even this operation can be cut by the use of balers, which feed and press the hay into a box until it is almost solid, tie it with wire, and eject it in the shape of an oblong bale.

There were no such farms in our immediate neighbourhood. Our hay, and that of our neighbours,

227

would have to be loaded by hand on to carts or wagons, led to stack-yards or Dutch barns, offloaded again, and built into stacks. The hay must be dry. If wet, it would ferment in the stack and possibly catch fire through spontaneous combustion. Speed then, when it came to leading, was essential. There must be two carts or wagons. There must be at least two persons, preferably four, on the field to pitch the hay on to the carts: one on the cart to "build" the load, two (and again, preferably four) to pitch to the stack, two on the stack (both experts) to do the building.

I knew all this in theory. That was how it had been in that part of Yorkshire where we had lived, and it had been the same in our part of Cornwall, where we had farmer neighbours, as well as seafaring ones, and I remember once asking the little boy who brought our milk how his father, who ran his holding single-handed, got his hay in.

"Oh, sir," the boy said, "other men come. *We helps they, and they helps we!*"

I knew we should need help. I didn't know where it would come from, but I was partly enlightened when, reporting for duty at Clow's meadow at eight o'clock next morning, wearing thick woollen pants under my riding breeches, and carrying my cushion, Clow said rather surlily :

"Let's make a start. There's Thomas of Hendre wants me to cut a four-acre meadow of his when I've done this, and there's the Jew's Harp expecting me with the tractor and trailer tomorrow. They've both got horses and wagons and they've done it before without a tractor, but they know I've got one now, and there's no getting out of it. *Jowl*, there'll be more of them wanting help. All we'll get out of it is our meals, and their help with our own hay when the time comes."

What more could we want, I thought, than that "we should help they, and they should help we"? But I didn't take Clow's grousing too seriously. Probably our neighbours (although I could not believe it of the folk at the Jew's Harp) would talk the same way. I was pleased that the Jew's Harp folk had asked for Clow's help. If they didn't include me, then I'd certainly volunteer, not because I wanted them to help us, but because I liked them.

It was another fine, warm day. I was still stiff and sore from my ordeal of yesterday, and I glanced at the seat of the mowing-machine a little apprehensively, as though it had been a dentist's chair. Clow's meadow was level and smooth, however. It was seed grass, and must have been rolled. There were no bumps, and although we went fast, nothing like so much vibration. I'd been broken in, too. I felt practised, quite an expert, and I was happy.

The job was soon finished, and we set off for Hendre. I had met Thomas of Hendre. He was one of the characters who had been in the Jew's Harp the night of our arrival. He was a short, tubby man, elderly, clean-shaven, with a jolly face. He was very quiet, unassuming in contrast to Clow, who put on his haughtiest condescending manner when we arrived. The boundaries of his farm came up to the Castlebridge road, opposite our own. The house (little more than a cottage) was about a mile south of Castle Druid, and we reached it by an accommodation lane.

The farm was bigger than most in the district, extending to nearly a hundred acres, and Thomas was a first-rate farmer, with a fine herd of pedigree cattle. He was handicapped by the fact that his only son had enlisted in the Navy at the outbreak of war, and his only male help was a labourer older than himself. He had twenty-five acres of grass to cut, and a horse-drawn mower.

"We'll show you how to mow grass," Clow swanked. "It's time you sold your horses, Thomas, and got a tractor. We'll have those four acres of yours down while you and old Willy are doing an acre."

Thomas smiled, and I fancied that there was a touch of irony in his voice when he answered quietly:

"Yes, indeed. They're wonderful things now. Perhaps I'll be getting one when the boy comes home, but it takes a clever man like yourself to handle such a thing. Will you have a drink of tea and a bite before you make a start? I'll tell my good lady you're here."

A woman had appeared at the farmhouse door, tubby and jolly-looking as Thomas himself. She greeted Clow affably (it seemed) in Welsh, and Clow condescended to smile. Thomas introduced me to her, and we shook hands. I was glad he had not introduced me as the squire. She was more talkative than her husband. She'd heard such a lot about the improvements we'd done at Castle Druid, and would like very much to call, but she had been afraid of doing so in case we thought she was intruding. I told her not to stand on ceremony, but to call whenever she liked, and meet my wife and the children, and have a row on the lake in our boat.

It was too early for dinner yet, but she brought out a huge jug of what she said was ginger beer, and a plate of cakes. It was a delicious drink, and I don't think ginger was its sole ingredient, for even Clow was grinning happily when he'd drunk his second mug.

"Come on now," he said. "Let's get on with it. One more mug for luck."

Like Clow's own field, the one we had to mow was level and smooth, and we'd got round it twice before Mrs Thomas waved to us that dinner was ready. Thomas himself was cutting the field next to it, with two horses yoked to his mower, and old Willy, it seemed, doing nothing but clear the swaths at the corners.

It was an enormous meal, with more beer. We went back to the job. By now—and the beer may have contributed to this—I had overcome all my distaste for the mowing-machine. I felt as tough as any farmer's boy, driving a cart and cracking a whip, and Clow still was in good humour, although he couldn't refrain from swanking, pointing to our own swaths, and then to Thomas, with his horses, moving so slowly on the other field.

"We'll have to take pity on the poor chap," he said generously, when we had to stop and fill up the tractor's fuel tank. "When we've finished this, we'll go and finish that one off for him. He's got a wagon, he'll have to come and help us lead, when ours is ready. You'd better tell your good lady to ask Mrs Thomas how to brew harvest beer if she doesn't know. We'll need a few gallons of it the day we lead."

We worked till dusk again.

The sun was shining when I woke next morning. Through the bedroom window came the smell of our own hay, which we hadn't touched since mowing. From the window the swaths looked completely dry. This was an illusion. When I went out and turned some of it with a fork, I saw that although the swaths were dry on top, underneath the grass was still green and moist, and I was alarmed. This business of "we helps they" was all right as long as "they" did help "we". It looked as though our meadow was all ready for turning, and we were to spend the day helping with the Jew's Harp hay. How long would the fine weather last?

Clow did not dispel my fears. He was not in a good mood when I joined him.

"That's how it is with haymaking and harvest, when you can't do everything for yourself, and you've got to have others to help. It's a nuisance, having to go and lead for the Jew's Harp, when we should be turning our own. But they've got in before us. It was the old lady who made Tom cut his hay last week. She's a sly one all right. But we'll turn the meadow tomorrow, and be damned to them all. Thomas of Hendre has promised the loan of his machine. He might have done the job for us, for what we did for him yesterday, but he didn't offer."

In spite of my fears, I was looking forward to helping at the Jew's Harp. The children had brought a message from them: the school was going to have a half-day holiday, Mano was going to help, and Amy was hoping that Dain and the elder children would come along too.

We drew up, with the tractor and trailer, outside the Jew's Harp at ten o'clock. Although the bar was shut for the sale of drinks, the street door was open, and from it came the smells of cooking. Clow didn't dismount from the tractor.

"Find out," he said, "which field they're leading first. We don't want to waste time and oil going to the wrong one."

I had of course told them at the Jew's Harp about our partnership. They had made no comment whatever. That, I thought, was politeness, and did not signify approval. Indeed, I was certain that Mother at least strongly disapproved, and with a little encouragement on my part would have told me so vehemently.

She was the only person in sight when I went in. She was standing in the passage leading to the kitchen. She had a walking-stick in her hand, was wearing a light cotton dress, with an apron made of a sack, and outdoor boots, and she was shouting in Welsh to Sara, who was evidently in the kitchen. She broke off when she saw me and smiled.

"Good morning, squire *bach*. I am very pleased to see you. Go into the best room now, and sit down. Will you have a cup of tea or a glass of beer? Tom and Amy are in the fields and I'll be there myself when I see that everything is all right in the kitchen."

She broke off to shout something else to the invisible Sara, and tapped her stick upon the ground as though to emphasise her words.

"If you want a thing done well you must do it for yourself. Sara has forgotten to put baking powder in the pastry. All my children are fools. They wouldn't have cut the grass for another week if I hadn't told them. Go into the parlour now. Will your lady and the children be coming?"

I told Mother that I was here with Clow and the tractor, and that Clow wanted to know which field we were to go to.

"That man!" she said tartly. "I told Tom that we'd be better off without him. But I'm glad that you have come."

Fortunately, Clow had left the engine running, and could not have heard these remarks. She told me the name of the field, and I told her that I was hoping that Dain and some of the children would be coming along in the milk lorry. She asked me to tell Tom that she herself would be coming along to the field very soon, and that he was not to start leading until she did.

The field was at the farthest boundary of the farm, abutting the river. Before we got there, I heard the sound of singing. Tom, with a horse rake, was sweeping the hay into windrows, and there were several women, including Amy and Mano, following with hand rakes, gathering every wisp the machine had missed. They were singing as they worked, in harmony, like a choir. A small wagon with two horses was waiting near the gate of the field, with two men standing by. One of them was a farmer I had not met. The other was the trampish-looking man who had been at the Jew's Harp bar, the night of our arrival.

Clow nodded curtly to the farmer as we drew up. The other was leering in the unpleasant manner of a drunkard. He spoke, but Clow ignored him. Although the man was almost in hearing, Clow said:

"That's Elijah Prophet, do you know him?"

"Only by sight."

"He's a waster. He's only here to see what he can pick up in the way of food and beer. That's his missus out there in the field with the others, the stout one."

The singing women were in the middle of the field. I could see a rather elderly one who fitted Clow's description.

Clow went on, grumbling:

"It's a bloody nuisance having to wait till tile old lady gets here before we make a start. She's a tartar. They're all afraid of her."

I didn't want to hear anything against Mother, and I said, for his remarks had aroused my curiosity:

"Tell me about Elijah. Is that his real name?"

"Yes, indeed. That's the name he draws his old age pension on, and he spends every penny of that on the drink, and that isn't enough for him. He's a lazy good-for-nothing."

The tractor was in between us and Elijah, and he could not have heard. In spite of his drunken, dissolute expression, he was standing quite erect. He was tall and thin. In one hand he held a long stick. He was not leaning on it.

"Is he a local man?"

"No. No one knows where he comes from, but he's Welsh. A tinker he was by trade, wandering round, mending pots and pans, but a beggar and a tramp really, although he was a soldier in the First War, and said he'd been a sergeant. It's twenty years since he came here. In winter time it was, and it was when things were bad and no one had any money, and maybe he was cold and hungry, with walking a long way over the hills. And there was Widow Phillips, alone in her cottage at the back end of the village. She had lost her man in the war, and had no children . . . Well, Elijah knocks on her door. It's a small cottage with only a loft above the living-room, and she has her bed downstairs where it's easier to keep warm in winter time—a double-bed which she covers with a quilt by day. Elijah didn't look so bad in those days. He wouldn't be drunk, for he had no money to buy the drink.

"Well, she opens the door. He's standing there in the cold, and because she's Welsh she asks him to come inside. He asks if she has any pots or pans she wants mending. She hasn't and he begs her then to give him a cup of tea and a bite. The fire is on, but there's no water in the kettle. The well is on the other side of the road, and she tells him to sit down by the fire while she goes and fills the kettle. She leaves the door open, and with a shawl over her head goes to the well. And when she comes back, there is Elijah stretched out full length on the bed with the quilt over him, fast asleep, or maybe just pretending.

"There's some women would have screamed and gone for the police. Gwen didn't. She had a soft heart, and she was a lonely woman, and she must have thought it was a miracle had happened, a man in her bed again.

And Elijah must have thought he was on to a good thing. He was fed up with wandering about, sleeping in barns and under hedges, never knowing where he was going to get his next meal. Gwen had her widow's pension. The cottage was hers, she was a good worker and a good cook. There was no other man in the village or the district likely to come her way. So she let him stay, and they got married. Elijah hasn't done a stroke of work since that day, beyond fetching water from the well, or chopping sticks for the fire. He'll pick up a fork or a rake and pretend to be haymaking today, but it's the beer he's after, while Gwen does the work for him . . . Well, here's the old lady coming along."

Mother was walking vigorously towards us. She had an old-fashioned sunbonnet on her head, a walking-stick in her hand. The faithful Nellie was by her side. There had been no need to give Tom her message. She walked into the field, poked at the hay with her stick, picked up a handful and examined it expertly. She waved her stick to Tom. He pulled up and she walked to him. Again she poked at the hay, then she waved her stick at us.

"She's satisfied," said Clow, moving to start the tractor engine. "We'll be leading from the far end. Jump on."

We went at full speed to the far end of the field, and stopped at the end of one of the windrows. The women left off their raking and gathered round us, and I thought then that I had never seen a happier, jollier crowd. Amy and Mano of course I knew well enough. And I must have seen Gwen before, but I looked at her now with special interest. She'd be about sixty-five, her hair nearly white. She didn't look as though she had ever been beautiful, but she had good teeth, a lovely smile, and she must have been attractive as a girl. Certainly there was nothing tragic in her face, as there was in poor widowed Sara's, nothing to suggest that she repented the bargain she had made.

We started to load, with Clow and one of the women on the trailer to do the stacking. Mother joined us, seized a fork herself and started work, sharply silencing Amy when she suggested that it would be bad for her rheumatics. The wagon drew up to the next windrow. Two more elderly men and another woman had joined us and were leading the wagon too. Elijah was making at least a token show of earning his beer. The women started to sing again.

I had learned how to use a hayfork in Yorkshire. It has a long shaft, and two thin, curved, sharply-pointed prongs or tines. You sweep the hay into a heap, roll it slightly, then press the prongs well down into the middle of it, compressing the hay inwards like a woman making dough. Then you heave it up on to the cart, give the handle a twist so that the curve of the tines is downwards, and pull them loose. Hay is surprisingly heavy when compressed, and as loading proceeds, you have to heave it higher. I had learned just how much I could lift at a time with tolerable ease. It was no more than Mother was lifting, yet twice as much as the crafty Elijah was doing, and we were doing two to his one.

We loaded long before the wagon, and when Clow had roped it, we started off for the stack, the foundations for which had been prepared at a corner of the field near the gate. As we reached it, I saw Dain and Amelia and Makubwa, helping Sara carry a milk can which I guessed was full of beer, and two baskets of food. Mary and Jane, holding Timothy by the hand, were coming along behind them, with some of the village children.

It was perfect haymaking weather. The sun was blazing hot, without a cloud in the blue sky. There was a gentle westerly wind with no moisture in it. It was a heavy crop. Tom had finished his raking. He was now ready to start stacking. The foundations of the stack had been prepared with a thick layer of old straw, on to which our first load was spread. Still more neighbours had arrived, mostly women, and they, with Sara, helped Tom with the stack, and they too soon were singing.

Sara called to us to have a drink before we set off for the next load. We responded. Clow, who hadn't spoken to any of the new arrivals, or to Dain or the children, was actually grinning as he moved to start the engine again, and he called to the children to climb on to the trailer for a ride. He lifted Timothy alongside of him on the tractor itself. We passed the wagon on our way. Elijah was walking with it. Clow winked at me.

"He's smelt the beer!"

It was hard work, requiring all one's strength and energy, but how good it was to see the field (it was a ten-acre one) becoming bare, to see the stack growing bigger, to see the children playing in the hay, to hear and join in (although I didn't know the words) the singing. There was bread, and cheese, and fresh-made Welsh cakes, beer, and tea for those who preferred it, at eleven o'clock. There was lemonade and a milder brew of ginger beer for the children. We went in relays to the Jew's Harp for dinner. Farmers were allowed extra rations for hay and harvest time. There was no shortage of anything.

The field was bare and the stack finished before the middle of the afternoon. The next field, which was nearer to the house, had to be led to the stackyard, which, with the farm buildings, was on the opposite side of the road to the pub. By then, some of the helpers had gone (presumably to attend to their own haymaking) but others, including Albert the Post, back from his rounds, had come to take their place.

Mother was still working (and singing) as lustily as anyone. Elijah, however, had been sitting since dinnertime in a shaded place in the stackyard, where incidentally the can of beer had been placed, in a state of blissful stupor. I was in a state of elation myself. It wasn't the beer that had produced it. It was the joy that came from working all out at a worthwhile job, from helping people I liked and admired, from the feeling they gave me of friendship and comradeship.

When we stopped for tea, Dain, who had been working as hard as anyone, said to me:

"Won't it be fun when we lead our own hay! Amy says they'll all be coming to help us. And Sara has told me how to make harvest beer. She's offered to help us with the baking too, but I think we can manage that all right. When do you think we shall do it?"

I asked Clow. Although he hadn't joined in the singing, and had held himself aloof from the others, particularly the women, he had taken his share of the refreshments, and had been in a good mood all day. True that he had been critical of the way Tom had built the stacks, but only to me in private. Perhaps he had been afraid of Mother, who watched the operation with an eagle eye, and several times gave her son advice.

"*Jowl*," he said. "If we hadn't had to come here today we could have had it tedded and into small cocks by nightfall. We could have broken the cocks tomorrow, gathered them again, and we could have been leading the day after. This job's going to take us till dark."

He was right, or nearly right. It was dusk when the last of the Jew's Harp hay was in, and nearly dark when I got home. Dain had gone back with the children long ago, and the children, of course, were all in bed. But it wasn't too dark for me to see that the whole of our own hay had not only been turned, but made into small cocks.

Dain and Porgy told me what had happened. Thomas of Hendre, his wife and the old man, had arrived just after lunch with their haymaking machine, and Porgy herself had helped them do the job.

We'd helped they. They had helped we.

It was fine next morning. It was the sort of weather which made one feel that it would never break, that the sun would go on shining day after day, that it could never rain again. Although there had been a night-dew, and the tops of the cocks were damp, it seemed to me that by the afternoon our crop should be ready for leading, if we shook out the cocks, spreading the hay in the sun.

Clow said no. Even if it were dry by then we couldn't do it. Everybody was haymaking now. Thomas Hendre would be busy on his own fields. We were lucky he'd been able to turn and cock ours while we'd been leading for the Jew's Harp. The Jew's Harp would be helping the man who helped them yesterday with his wagon. Tomorrow was the earliest we could lead. What we must do today was to break the cocks and make them into big cocks before nightfall, let everyone know we were ready, and hope for the best about them coming. We'd need plenty of food and drink ready "in case".

We had no rake or haymaking machine. We had to do the whole job by hand, lifting each cock with a fork and spreading the hay round as thinly as possible. Porgy and Dain gave a hand in spells, but they had started their baking and the brewing of the beer, and for most of the time Clow and I were working on our own. There was none of the excitement of yesterday, there was no singing, no beer, and the job seemed interminable. There seemed to be thousands of little cocks to be broken up and spread. Then, soon after dinner, a young man arrived on a bicycle, with an urgent request for Clow and his tractor and trailer to go to another farm.

"I'll have to do it," Clow grumbled. "But there'll be no need for you to come. You'll have to finish it by yourself. Start making the big cocks when you get to the end of these. It'll take you all your time to get it done before dark."

This was "help they" with a vengeance.

Dain and Porgy came to the rescue again during the afternoon. The children, too, helped when they got back from school, but by then I had only made a start on the big cocks. I couldn't help thinking that it was a waste of time and energy making them. The hay was all perfectly dry. If we were to lead tomorrow (and we had sent a message with Albert to the Jew's Harp that we were ready) the cocks would have to be broken and spread and the whole crop raked again. Surely in weather like this it wasn't necessary?

All day the sky had been a clear blue, with only the gentlest wind to temper the intense heat of the sun. Several times I had stopped to take a quick plunge in the lake. And when the call for supper came, I decided to go in again, for the wind had dropped completely and I was dripping with sweat. It was when I climbed out that I realised for the first time that the sun, although it had lost none of its power, was veiled. The sky was no longer blue but pale grey.

I was alarmed. I hadn't made more than a dozen cocks. At least nine-tenths of the field was flat. I hurried to the house. The kitchen window was wide open.

"I think it's going to rain," I yelled. "Come and help, as many as you can!"

I ran to where I had made the last cock, and started another. Dain, Parkey, Amelia, Makubwa joined me, raking up the hay while I did the cocking. The sun now looked like a harvest moon. The sky above had no definite cloud, but in the east was a low dark grey mass, almost like a range of mountains, with one peak which gleamed white, like a snow field. I heard the first low rumble of thunder.

We worked frantically. The bank of cloud was rising rapidly. I saw flashes of lightning ripping across it. The thunder grew louder. The sun was still red like the harvest moon, but wisps of cloud, the advance guard of the storm, were sweeping overhead and to the west, and soon it was as though the sun had set. Darkness began to fall. And then, after one loud thunderclap, it started to rain.

18

IT WAS not a particularly violent thunderstorm. It had passed over before midnight. There was not a very heavy rainfall, but it rained all night, and it was raining the next morning. The hay that had been crisp and dry when I started making the cocks was flat and sodden, and the sight of the score or so of cocks I had succeeded in making, gave me small comfort. If the rain went on the hay in them would become as sodden as the rest.

And, just as it had been difficult yesterday to imagine that the fine weather would ever break, now it was difficult to believe that the sky would ever be blue again, the sun shining. Clow was not encouraging.

"If it goes on like this for a week, the damned stuff won't be worth picking up," he growled. "All the goodness will be washed out of it. It will turn mouldy. The old lady at the Jew's Harp knew what she was doing when she had hers cut a week ago. Every bit of it in, and as dry as a bone. She'll not do it on us like that next year, by damn."

He had walked over late in the morning, and we were standing in the portico of the mansion. The younger children, with Parkey, were at their lessons in the drawing-room. Dain and Porgy in the kitchen were wondering, I supposed, what to do with the piles of cakes and sandwiches they had prepared for today's haymaking. It was, indeed, a dismal scene that we surveyed. The sky was leaden. A mist obscured the tops of the hills. There was no wind. The rain fell vertically but steadily. I had my oilskins on, for I had been coming up from the garden when I had seen Clow.

"I suppose," I said with an attempt at cheerfulness, "there's nothing we can do but wait for it to be fine again. It can't rain forever, can it?"

"It will not stop raining today," he answered. "But what we can do is to go down to Dai's and take the wheel to pieces, and get it on the trailer, and bring it to where it's got to be. And if it goes on raining, we can get the pit built. When I got home last night, I found a letter from my sister that Albert had pushed under the door. It had come by airmail. There wasn't any more money in it, by damn, but then, I didn't expect any. She was very pleased to get my letter telling her about the lake, and she asks if we can have a photo taken of it, and the boat and the little ones in it, and bathing. It must look very beautiful, she says, and she thinks it is a fine idea having a waterwheel and lighting up the mansion with electricity. But I told her we'd have to leave the wheel for when we could spare time from farming. Come on now, let us get on with it while we have the chance. *Jowl*, I'd like to send her a photo of that, when we get it fixed, and one of the mansion. She says again she'll be coming to see it all when the war's over."

The waterwheel had never been out of mind. It was ironic to think that I could now, thanks to the rain that looked like ruining our hay crop, consider getting on with it without a twinge of conscience. There was nothing I could do in the garden today. It would be no use trying to weed the crops, for the soil would be like mud. If Clow was eager, so was I, only more so, for the wheel would be the fulfilment of my ambition. I did not suspect that behind his eagerness was an even stronger ambition.

I said to him:

"Righto. Let's do it. We'll need some tools, won't we?"

"We'll need spanners, and a hammer and cold chisel, in case we've got to cut some of the bolts. An axe or saw for that tree locking the wheel. I'll bring the lifting tackle. You'd better bring some grub with you. It will take us most of the day, and Dai's not the man to give us a feast."

It was nearly noon, and it was still raining when we arrived at the mill. The cottage door was shut, and I knocked on it. It was not until I had knocked again, and louder, that there was a sleepy shout, in Welsh from within. Dai apparently was still in bed. I shouted my name, and that Clow and I were here to start taking the wheel to pieces. Was it all right?

"Yes, indeed," came the answer. "Please do what you like."

Clow winked at me.

"Not up yet, eh?" he said. "*Jowl*. It's queer how those

246

who do the least work seem to need the most rest. Poetry! That man ought to have had a stick across his bottom when he was a youngster, and made to do some honest work. What's the use of poetry writing?"

It was a question I was not tempted to answer at that moment, or I might have said in defence of Dai that if he hadn't been a poet he wouldn't have so readily given us his waterwheel. The sight of the wheel had revived all the excitement I had felt when I had first seen it with Dain and the children. The ash tree growing between its spokes had then been in bud. Now it was in full leaf, and the ground all round the pit was almost breast high with stinging nettles. Spreading above the wheel were the branches of a large oak.

I opened the gate in the surrounding wall. Clow backed the trailer through the nettles until it was alongside the outer wall of the wheel pit, which luckily was almost level with the trailer floor. I was wearing shorts under my oilskins, and I warily followed the wheel tracks through the nettles to join Clow on the pit wall. He was looking at the wheel in the same way as he had looked at the bulging wall of the mansion before he had tackled it with his crowbar.

"We're in luck," he said. "This is going to be easy. It's in four sections. All we've got to do is to take out the bolts, and hoist the sections up one at a time and swing them on to the trailer. Let's have the spanners and make a start."

But it was not easy. The bolts were rusted. They were awkwardly sited, so that it was difficult to get our spanners on to them, difficult to turn them when we did.

One of us had to grip the head of the bolt, the other the nut, both of us exerting our full strength in opposite directions.

The rain continued, but it was too warm and close for us to work in oilskins. It pelted down our necks when we bent. It fell in heavier drops from the overhanging trees, and to add to our discomfort, there were swarms if midges, biting our faces and hands. Some of the bolts resisted all our efforts with the spanners. We had to cut the nuts with the chisel.

We had been working about an hour when we heard a shout. Dai, holding a large umbrella over his head, was standing at the gate. He had a steaming jug in his other hand.

"I thought that you might like a drink of tea," he said. "I would ask you to come in out of the rain, but my house is so untidy, and I've been too busy to clear it up. I've been writing."

"It's very kind of you," I said. "I hope we haven't disturbed you, coming like this."

"No, indeed. Nothing disturbs me when I'm writing my poetry."

He hadn't looked at, nor did he seem to take the slightest interest in, the waterwheel. He put the jug down on the wall, went back to the cottage and returned with two mugs. Again I thanked him, and Clow spoke to him in Welsh, but he hurried away and I heard the sound of his door closing.

"He's looney," Clow said. "There's no one yet been inside his door, not even Albert the Post. He always keeps the door locked and curtains across his windows."

We crouched under the trailer to drink our tea and eat our food. There was no temptation to linger over it. We were soaked to the skin. The midges were relentless. We had by now succeeded in extracting all the bolts of one quarter section. We had cut away the ash tree growing through the spokes. The overhanging branch of the oak was very thick. Clow swarmed up the trunk and fixed the steel block of the hoisting tackle immediately above the wheel. He hooked the fall to the loose section. We hoisted it clear, and with another rope swung it sideways on to the trailer.

We started work on the bolts of the next section. The rain eased off a little, changing to a drizzle. It made little difference to our physical discomfort, for it still dripped from the tree, and the midges were now joined by swarms of flies, buzzing about us. Clow made no complaint, however. I had never known him in a happier mood.

"It's in good condition," he said, "and yet it must be at least fifty years old. With new boards, and a couple of coats of paint on this ironwork, it will be as good as new. A thing like this would cost us a couple of hundred pounds if we had it made today. It's a pity we haven't got the pit and the sluice built. I could have had it in, mounted and turning round with the water by tomorrow night. We'll want a photograph of it to send to Gwen."

His use of the "us" and "we" and "I" in relation to the waterwheel irritated me. The wheel was not "his" or "ours" but mine. Doubtless when he wrote to his sister about the mansion, the lake, and now the wheel, he was taking credit for all that we had done. But it was a passing irritation.

My own enthusiasm was in no degree diminished. The picture I had of the turning wheel, of the lights burning in the house, was as bright as ever. Yet I did think that Clow was being over-optimistic. The pit wasn't built, the sluice wasn't made. The boards for the buckets had to be sawn and fitted. I hadn't worked out yet how I was going to connect up the driving shaft of the dynamo. And, although I could put up with the wet, the annoyance of the midges and flies, I knew that I wouldn't have protested if, after we had got the second section on board the trailer, he had decided to call it a day—for the drizzle had changed to rain again, and it was becoming cold.

To get at the bolts of the two remaining sections, he had to unbolt the axle bearings, and hoist up the whole thing clear of the pit. It was too heavy to swing on to the trailer in one piece. We bridged the pit with two logs and let it rest on these while we removed the bolts, everyone of which defied the spanners, and had to be cut out with the chisel. It must have been well past teatime when the last of them was out, and the two sections loaded on to the trailer. There was still the cogwheel shaft, which passed through the wall into the old mill building.

I had been listening hopefully for a shout from Dai that he had made us another jug of tea. There was no sign of him, however, and I lacked the courage to go and knock at his door. But I had the courage to say to Clow when we went into the mill, and saw that the shaft was buried under the debris of the fallen roof:

"It will be a long time before we need the shaft. Don't

you think we could leave it until another day?"

The rain had suddenly stopped. A wind had sprung up, stirring the tops of the trees, and I was shaking with cold.

"No, dammit," he answered inexorably, "that will mean another trip. We've got to finish the job now we've started it. We may not get another chance. The weather's changing. It feels to me like a north wind blowing. If it clears up we may be haymaking tomorrow. Come on, let's get on with it."

The most agreeable of dreams can lose their inspiration when you are cold, tired and hungry. At that moment I felt that I would have bartered my waterwheel and all it signified, for a hot bath, warm dry clothes, a cup of tea. But as soon as we started to clear the rubble, I felt better. We began at the foot of the wall nearest to where the wheel had been, where the rubble was not so thick, and, finding the shaft, we worked along it.

It was an iron rod, two inches in diameter. It would have led, I guessed, to the grinding stones, where, as one of them rotated horizontally, there would have been a bevelled gear and a vertical shaft. But the stones had been removed. In any case they would have been buried feet deep in the rubble, and I was certain that all I needed for my dynamo, or any other machinery, was six clear feet of shaft on to which I could mount a belt or an iron spur wheel.

I was to have no choice about this, however. Four feet away from the wall the shaft ended. There must have been a coupling here, and the remainder of the shaft taken away by those who had removed the stones. We returned to the pit. Clow seized the cogwheel, gave it a turn or two, and the whole shaft came out. He carried it to the trailer. He rubbed his hands on his trousers then, and took out his watch.

"Only six o'clock," he said. "It'll take us half an hour to drive back and get it offloaded. We can start work building the pit. We won't be able to do that tomorrow if it's fine."

My spirits had risen again. The wind was cold, but overhead between the treetops there were patches of blue sky, and the glint of sunshine on the wet leaves. The wheel had been successfully dismantled. It was going to be very exciting putting it together again, finally getting it to work. A hot bath, a change of garments and a meal, and I'd be prepared to work till nightfall on the building of the pit.

Clow was lashing the load. I heard the clatter of hooves on the road, and there was Amelia and Mary and Makubwa on our ponies. They pulled up at the gate, and at the same time Dai, without his umbrella, appeared. He did not so much as glance at us or the dismantled wheel. But he beamed at Amelia and said:

"Have you read the little poem I gave you, Amelia?"

Amelia was blushing.

"Yes, I have. And I've learnt it by heart, but I don't quite know what it means."

Dai laughed.

"Don't let that bother you. In poetry it is the words, and the rhythm that matter. The beautiful Welsh words, each syllable like a music note. Listen to this now . . ."

He began to recite again, and it was unfortunate that

Clow—and I don't think that he did it with the deliberate purpose of cutting Dai short—started the tractor engine. Amelia was mounted on one of the Welsh ponies. It reared, but she quickly mastered it. Dai, scared, had moved out of the way. I went to him, thanked him for letting us have the wheel, repeated our invitation to come to Castle Druid and see the lake, the wheel too, when we had got it installed.

He was smiling again.

"Yes, indeed, I will come when I can find the time. There is so much to do. So much to write. Wait now, I must find some apples for the children. I think I have some left."

He disappeared again. He came back with some apples and a sheet of paper, which he handed to Amelia.

"Another poem for you. And that one is written to you, the little English girl, with a bunch of primroses in her hand in the springtime."

Clow was driving the tractor and trailer through the gateway, and he was signing to me to jump up. He shouted something to Dai in Welsh, which may have been, and I hoped it was, an expression of his personal gratitude. Dai answered briefly, and, it seemed, genially, but he didn't give a glance at the trailer and its load. It was as though the waterwheel, so exciting to me, for him had no significance whatever. It might have been a load of kitchen refuse we were carting away.

He was a poet. Whether he was good, bad, or indifferent, I could not say, for I could not read Welsh. But there was nothing spurious about him, nothing of the poseur, nothing of the boaster. Clearly he wrote for the sheer love of it, oblivious of everything but his muse.

I jumped on to the trailer, Clow turned into the road and the children followed like mounted escort, a munching their apples. We all, except Clow, looked back when we came to the bend in the road. Dai stood watching us, smiling. We waved to him and he waved back, and Amelia, clutching her precious poem, called to me:

"Oh, he is a nice man. I just love him." And I felt the same myself.

19

THERE WAS no rain during the night. It was a fine morning, with racing, summery clouds and a cool moderate northwest wind. It looked as though yesterday's rain, and the thunderstorm of the previous night, had been nothing more than a temporary break in the spell of settled weather. We'd get our hay in all right, and it would have taken little harm from its wetting.

It was still wet, however, at nine o'clock (double summer time) when Clow arrived. There was dew on it, as well as rain, and the cocks were actually steaming.

"We can't touch it yet," he said, "except for breaking up the cocks you made and spreading them out. But I've got the loan of a rake and a tedder for this afternoon, and if the weather keeps like this, we'll get it turned, and into cocks again by nightfall, and we may get it led tomorrow. We'll get on with the pit until dinnertime, and then have another look at it."

He was in a very good mood. We broke up and spread the cocks. As we walked down to the lake, he remarked:

"My, it's a picture, that. A real picture. I told you it needed the lake to show the place off. If only Rosie could see it. You won't forget about taking some photos of it, will you? Have you got a camera?"

It did not strike me that there was anything unusual or significant in his request. Naturally his sister would like to see photos of Castle Druid. Naturally he would like to give her visual proof of what he had told her in his letters.

I had a camera, but it had been difficult to get films during the war. I promised I would take some photos as soon as possible.

"And one of the mansion, too. Front view, of course, not the back. It's a pity you haven't got the front garden made. I'll give you a hand with that when you say the word. It ought to be all flowers there, and a nice gate."

We paused at the dam wall, looking at the lake. It was beautiful! Although the volume of the stream pouring over the spillway had increased with the rain, the water in the lake was still crystal clear. There were catspaws of wind on its surface in the middle, but near the bank, where Makubwa had caught his eel, it was like a mirror, so that you could hardly detect the dividing line between the real bank and its reflection. Thus it had been in our Cornish creek on a fine summer's day. The sight of

255

the dinghy, moored to the trunk of a tree close by, made the resemblance more vivid, evoking in me a sudden sharp nostalgia for our old Cornish home, for the salty smell of the real sea. For one second it was as though I was there. Then Clow brought me back to reality.

"Come on, let's make a start. We've got a lot to do."

We had offloaded the sections of the waterwheel as close to our chosen site as Clow could move the trailer. Before we had knocked off last night, we had made considerable progress with the excavation of the bank.

The pit should be ten feet in length, five feet wide, five feet deep, but for the width we had to allow an extra foot on each side of the walls, which would have to be very strongly built to support the axle.

We were out of sight of the lake here, and there was nothing to distract my mind. I had a clear conscience, too. We were only doing this because the hay was too wet for working on. I had already done all the poultry chores. There was nothing particularly urgent to do in the vegetable garden. The soil would still be too wet for any weeding in the fields.

We worked with pickaxe and shovel, like navvies. The pit would be parallel to the stream, but its farther end had to be open, with a gulley joining the stream to take the water that spilt from the stream itself. It was hard work. It was not only soil we had to remove. There were stones, some of them quite big, which had to be levered out with the crowbar. And there were roots from nearby trees, one of them an oak, more difficult to remove than the rocks.

But how pleasant it was to be doing this in dry

weather, without the rain dripping on us as it had done yesterday, during the dismantling of the wheel and during the building of the dam wall. There were no midges to bite us, and not so many flies.

It was exciting too. My dream of owning a working waterwheel was coming true at last. We were not going to finish it today. It might indeed be weeks, even months, before the climax came, and the wheel was turning and working. But every shovelful of soil, every stone we removed, was progress toward that end. And it didn't worry me that Clow obviously considered himself in command of the operation.

"You're getting in my way," he said, when we had got about three feet down at the end of the pit nearest the dam wall. "You'd best start gathering stones for the walls. There's plenty of them in the stream. Bring them up and put them handy for me. Only clean, square stones. We've got to make a decent job of it."

It was getting on for lunchtime when Dain appeared on the dam wall, and then came down towards us. She was looking very excited, and at first didn't seem a bit interested in what we had done. She had a letter m her hand.

"Albert has been," she cried, "and he's brought two huge parcels. They're from your sister in Canada, Clow. There are some wonderful Canadian clothes for the children, and toys, and sweets, and food. And such a lovely letter."

Clow had stood up in the pit, and was smiling a little self-consciously.

"Rosie told me in her letter she was sending some

things to you, but I didn't tell you in case they were sunk by the Germans, and you were disappointed. I'm glad they've arrived all right. But you keep those things for your own little ones, ma'am. Don't waste them on the evacuees. Did she say anything about wanting photos taken?"

"Yes she does. She'd like one of the mansion and the lake. She'd like one of you too, Clow, she says."

Clow laughed.

"Me? You wouldn't want to break the camera, would you? But I'd like the mansion and the lake taken, and the waterwheel too, when it's finished."

"You're getting on with it, aren't you? Albert brought a message from the Jew's Harp. Tom will be coming to help with the hay this afternoon, if it keeps fine. It's getting beautifully dry again. Dinner's nearly ready. Won't you come and join us for once, Clow, and see what your sister has sent?"

"No, thank you, ma'am. If Tom's coming out then I'll get back to my own hay and get it turned, and then come back here later. It's a pity we've got to leave this now, but hay's got to come first. But it won't be long before I've got the wheel going for you. Yes, we'll want a photo of that too."

Dain was right about the parcels. They were exciting, although the problem of sharing out their contents was a delicate one. We could not reserve any of them for our own children. The sweets could be shared, but there were checked and striped parkas and shirts and jeans. There were summer frocks, boots and shoes and stockings, some "used", some brand new—all with a characteristic

Canadian stamp about them. The only fair thing would be to draw lots when there was any competition, and the choice wasn't decided by size and fitting.

The letter, too, was charming. Clow, in his own letter to her, must have given her a very flattering account of us, especially of Dain. We were helping to beat the Germans. She was delighted that we were bringing the waste land of Castle Druid into cultivation again. It was wonderful to think that we had rebuilt the old mansion, and made a happy home for the poor children of the bombed cities. They were chiefly summer clothes she was sending, but she was asking all her friends to make contributions, and she would be sending parcels of winter clothing in the fall. She was looking forward so much to visiting us when the war was over. It would please her very much to see some photographs of the place and of us and her brother. Dain hadn't mentioned to Clow that she had added a postscript:

"Clow is a bit of a boaster. Don't take any notice. He's got a heart of gold."

Tom arrived soon after dinner with the horse and tedder. The weather was still fine. The top moisture had already dried from the hay. A tedder is a machine with rotating light steel tines which lift the mown grass and lightly toss it over, and tedding is a one-man operation with tractor or horse. But as the field was big, and it looked as though Tom would be a long time getting round it, I started work with a fork which was slower still, but better than doing nothing. It wasn't long before

Dain and Porgy joined me.

Tom had told us that he and Amy, and quite a lot of those who had been helping with Jew's Harp hay, would be coming tomorrow for the leading, unless of course it rained again; and it didn't look as though there was much chance of that. Only you never knew!

You certainly didn't. The sky was blue, the clouds, if a little ragged, were thin and white as they passed overhead in the cool dry north wind. Even the underneath of the swaths of hay seemed almost dry as we turned them. The smell was deliciously sweet. By teatime we'd get well over two-thirds of the field turned. Clow arrived, with his borrowed tedder. Tom offered to stay on and help us finish the turning, and then make the cocks, but Clow thanked him and said no. We could finish the job ourselves and we'd be ready for leading in the morning.

With the tractor going full out he finished the turning in less than an hour. The weather was still fine.

"We'll leave this now," he said then, "and go and cock my bit, and come back with the rake, and we'll have it all cocked before dark."

He uncoupled the tedder and we drove round to his own field. It was a thicker crop than ours and it was bone dry. He started on it at once, raking it into windrows, which I began to make into big cocks. When he finished the raking, he joined me. It must have been nearly seven when the last of the cocks was made.

In the last hour I had noticed that the driving clouds, instead of being white and translucent, were growing thicker and moving more slowly. The wind was less cold and it was blowing fitfully. Indeed, as we walked towards the tractor again, there was no wind at all, and Clow suddenly stopped and looked at the sky. The sun was shining, but it was through a gap in the clouds.

"*Jowl*," he said, "I don't like the look of it. It looks almost like rain. Come on, we've got to hurry back or we're going to have our hay wet again."

He started the engine. I jumped on, and away we went. But, by the time we had reached the Castle Druid gate, it was spotting with rain. The whole sky was overcast. Clow raked one row of that beautifully dry hay. Feverishly, I made one cock. But before I had gathered enough for another one, it was raining hard. Our afternoon's work had been for nothing.

It was not a thunderstorm. The rain had stopped before I went to bed that night, and the stars were shining in a clear sky. It was exasperatingly fine again the next morning—a perfect day for leading, had the hay been dry. It was not so sodden as it had been the morning after the thunderstorm, but it would have to be tedded again at least twice, and we wouldn't be able to touch it again until the afternoon. Leading was out of the question.

"It would have been all right if we'd had it cocked," Clow said. "All we'd need have done was take the tops off them. Mine will be all right."

I had been thinking that. If, instead of going to Clow's field, we had stayed on, and accepted Tom's offer of help, we could have had it all cocked before the rain came. Yet I couldn't blame Clow. He hadn't known that it was going to rain. And in any case, it was reasonable that he should give his own priority. I felt worried, all the same. Probably he would now take priority in leading. His hay was of course outside the partnership.

It was ten o'clock when he arrived. "Have you taken off the tops?" I asked.

"Yes. If it keeps fine I can have it all in the yard this afternoon. I'll tell Albert to let the Jew's Harp know. What we'll do is ted this as soon as it's dry enough on top. Then go up and lead mine. That won't take more than three hours, for it will all go into the barn. There's no stack to build. We'll be back here and ted this again, with the Jew's Harp to help, and we'll get it cocked for certain. And we might as well be getting on with the pit while we're waiting."

For once I felt no enthusiasm about the waterwheel. Even the lake, looking so beautiful as ever in the sunshine, with the trout plopping on its surface, failed to excite me. I was very worried. We had spent a lot of money on the meadow, for we had had it dressed with lime and fertiliser. It was vital that we should have a store of hay for winter feed for the cows. The weather was almost exactly the same as it had been yesterday, with light clouds and a northerly wind. And most likely it would follow the same pattern, turning to rain towards the end of the day, or perhaps before. Would it be possible to lead Clow's hay and get ours dry and into cocks before it happened? Today should have been our leading day, not Clow's. All our food and drink was ready. The beer would keep, but the cakes and pies that Dain and Porgy had made would be getting stale.

Clow apparently did not share my anxiety. He got into the pit, and started work where he had left off yesterday when Dain had come to tell us about the parcels, and again he told me to get on with the collecting of building stones.

"Have you remembered about those photographs?" he remarked shortly. "If it's just a matter of the expense, I don't mind paying for them. You said you'd got a camera, didn't you?"

"Yes, but no film. I haven't forgotten. We're trying to get one. And I'll certainly take them as soon as we do, and send them to your sister."

I had indeed written to a press photographer friend of mine, asking if he could get me a couple of films, for a very urgent job. The letter should be collected by Albert this morning for posting.

"*Jowl*," he said, "that's good. She'll be pleased to see them. We're almost deep enough now. I'll start the wall from this end. It'll only need a dozen more stones to start with. Then you'd better be getting on with the wood sluice, or the planks for the buckets. We're going to need about two score of new bolts for the wheel, in place of those we cut. You'll have to order them from Eddy. We don't want to be held up by anything when we get the pit finished. Have you thought out yet how you're going to fix the dynamo? Maybe I'll be able to do that for you, but it'll take some thinking out. It will have to be geared up somehow or other."

He was irritating me again, not with his orders, but by his obvious assumption that he was the authority on everything connected with the wheel. I hadn't yet worked out how I was going to fix the dynamo, but I did want to think it out for myself. It was not his concern at all.

"I think I can manage the dynamo all right, thank you," I said stiffly, "once the wheel is finished. I'll get on with the sluice when you've got all the stones you need. The planks are up at the house."

I left him shortly, to walk up to the house. I did not as much as glance at the lake, and the sight of the meadow did nothing to make me feel more cheerful. I picked up a handful of hay. It was drying on top, but was still damp underneath. It wasn't ready for turning yet.

Dain was with the children, playing games on the sunny side of the house, which we had left clear of the mown hay. I told her rather gloomily what Clow proposed to do.

"Well, that's all right," she laughed. "Especially if the Jew's Harp people will be there. Clow won't have been able to do any cooking. We'll be able to take our food and the beer up there, so that it won't be wasted after all, and we can bake again for tomorrow. We will get ours in tomorrow for certain."

I wished that I could have believed her.

I carried my planks down to the dam wall, and started making the sluice. It was to be a trough, fourteen feet in length, four feet wide, eight inches deep, and it would extend on a timber staging from the shuttered gap in the dam wall to a point a little beyond the highest point of the wheel. It was a simple job of carpentry, of measuring, sawing and nailing; and seeing what its purpose was, I should have been very happy doing it.

264

But I wasn't. I couldn't keep my mind off the hay. I kept on looking up at the sky, dreading that I should see a darkening of the clouds, and it vexed me that Clow was calmly working at the wall, and apparently not worried at all.

It wasn't long before he shouted to me that he wanted some more stones. He had finished the first course of one of the walls, and as I knew that he expected praise, I gave it to him.

"You're making a good job of it."

"Yes," he admitted, "I'll build a wall with anyone. When this is finished, it will last forever. I'd have the whole job done in a couple of days if there was nothing else to do."

"I suppose we'll have to knock off soon and start the hay," I said hopefully.

"Give it a chance, man," he answered. "It'll need another hour yet. Hurry up with the stones."

We started immediately after dinner and we were soon joined by Thomas Hendre, with his horse-drawn tedder. There was no sign of a change in the weather and my spirits were rising, for although it was still a little damp underneath, the hay rose easily from the machines, and was actually blowing in the wind. It looked and smelt like hay again, and it seemed no worse for its double soaking. It was all turned by three o'clock.

Clow had brought the trailer. As we expected that the Jew's Harp folk and Clow's other helper would be returning to help us with the cocking, we took only half the beer and food. I heard singing again as we drew near to Clow's field, but it stopped when we arrived. There was Tom, and Amy, and Gwen Prophet (but not Elijah, who must have assumed that Clow's fare would not be worth it), two other village women, and the youth who had come to call Clow away the afternoon of the thunderstorm. They had been sitting down in the hedge. Now they got up and greeted us. Clow gave them a condescending smile, but said nothing.

We unloaded the food and drink, and Dain proudly handed it round. It was the first time that she had acted as hostess in a hay field. Her Welsh cakes and the beer were pronounced excellent. We began the leading. There was only the trailer to do it, so we loaded it and followed it to the barn, pitching it in, and then returning for the next load.

Although they were, with the exception of the youth, the same people who had seemed so happy and jolly when they had been working on the Jew's Harp field — and they were just as energetic — they were mostly silent now. There was no singing, no joking. I couldn't believe that this was due to any lack of potency in the beer, which, on Sara's instructions, had been laced with strong ale. I felt that it was Clow himself who was unconsciously imposing constraint upon them. He'd only been one of many helpers at the Jew's Harp. Here he was boss, and he could not help showing it, not in the way of giving orders, for these were unnecessary, but in the look of superiority on his face, particularly when he was driving his tractor.

I had the impression that although they were working hard enough, they were only doing so from a sense of obligation, helping Clow because he had, or would, "help they". At the Jew's Harp I had felt gloriously happy. Now I did not. And soon I had a stronger reason for not doing so. The clouds were becoming edged with dark grey, exactly as they had done yesterday, but at a later hour. I saw Clow glancing at them too, long before we had got one half of the field led. He looked less pleased with himself.

"We'll have to hurry," he said to me, "if we're going to get this in and the other cocked before it rains again." And to the others he shouted something in Welsh. They all looked at the sky.

No matter how much they may have disliked Clow, their communal sense of duty must have been stronger. Here was good hay, fodder for the cows in the winter months, all beautifully dry; safe, once it was in the shelter of the barn. And in the sky was the threatening rain, the common enemy. It was Amy who gave a shout in Welsh, almost like a battle cry, and she began to sing *Land of our Fathers*, and we all joined in, pitching the hay as we sang at such a rate that Clow, on the trailer, was almost buried in it.

For the time being I did not think of our own hayfield, all dry again, more vulnerable to the rain than this, not even in little cocks. The wind had dropped. The whole sky was darkening. Any moment now the rain was going to break.

We got that load in, and another, and at last there was only one load left. I knew, as we hurried back to the field to rescue it, that there was not a hope of getting ours cocked. I felt the first drops of rain on my face. They were intermittent, and as yet could do no harm. We all worked frantically. And I had the satisfaction of pitching the last forkful on to the loaded trailer as Clow went at top speed for the barn.

Dain had run to the hedge, where she had left what remained of the food and the beer. The youth went to help her bring it along to the barn. There was just room in this for Clow to back the loaded trailer into it, and we all crowded in too, as the rain began to patter on the iron roof.

We had won, and if we had also lost it still didn't seem to matter. The beer was handed round. Led by Amy, the women started to sing, and this time a hymn, and I noticed that Clow, if he wasn't singing, was at least smiling at everyone with benevolence, as well he might.

20

I HAD READ somewhere that a British farmer's most vital asset should be the possession of nerves of iron. I was to appreciate the wisdom of this during the days that followed the successful leading of Clow's hay. For a whole week, with only one exception, there were clear skies every morning and afternoon. We tedded and re-tedded our hay, and it was dry. Then, just as we were ready to cock it, the rain came, not always heavy or lasting rain, but sufficiently heavy and sufficiently lasting to wet it thoroughly again.

My nerves were not of iron. I began to hate the very sight of our meadow. And it was no consolation to me to know that every farmer in the neighbourhood (except, of course, the Jew's Harp and Clow himself) was in the same plight. Nor did I find much consolation in the fact that the weather enabled us to get on with the waterwheel. My heart was not in it. I couldn't get the hay out of my mind.

Clow *had* nerves of iron. He grumbled each time the rain came, but I don't think it seriously worried him, certainly not as much as it did me. Dain, too, maintained her customary optimism. She was certain that we would get a spell of really dry weather soon, and that we would get it stacked in the end. It wasn't as though it was continuous rain. It wasn't getting mouldy yet. Each time it had dried it had smelt sweet and good. That was true, but for me it was more tantalising. If only we could get two clear days without rain!

Clow finished the walls of the pit. Eddy had sent a precious bag of cement with the bolts I had ordered, and we had used this for the top courses of the walls, and for fixing the axle bearings which we had brought from the mill. I had finished the sluice, but the supports for it had to wait for the completion of the walls, and I had started making the wood shutters for the buckets, which would be fitted when the wheel was reassembled.

How exciting all this would have been if, whenever I had to leave it and walk up to the house, I could have looked at the bare meadow all green again with short grass on which our cows and ponies would be grazing, and the hay in one big stack. Up in Yorkshire I had known seasons where the hay in most of the fields had lain so long that the young grass had grown through it, and it had just been left to rot. Was this going to happen with ours?

There was no convenient branch overhanging the pit, as there had been at the mill, but there were forked trees on either side of the stream, and Clow rigged up a sort of gantry, with a thick oak sapling fixed between to take the hoisting gear. We reassembled the two sections of the wheel which had been the last to come out of the original pit. To these was bolted the heavy steel axle. We hoisted it up, controlling it with skids and side lines until it was above the pit, and then gently lowered it until the ends of the axle rested in the bearings. We slackened off the gear, and Clow tested the alignment of the axle and bearings by seizing the half-wheel and giving it a powerful push. It swung back like the pendulum of a clock, and went on swinging, backwards and forwards, until its momentum was exhausted.

"Couldn't be better," he swanked. "Not if you'd had a firm of engineers on the job. When we get the other sections bolted on, that wheel will turn as sweet as a top. It's a pity we can't finish the job now, but we'll have to ted the hay again."

This was on the fourth day of that, to me, nerve-racking week. It had become a drill. Clow would arrive about ten, look at the field, pronounce it too wet to touch. We'd work at the wheel until dinnertime, then give the hay its first turning, and then go alone to Thomas Hendre, who with many more acres to deal with (none led and only one field cocked) was very glad of our help. We'd return always to find the hay just not quite dry enough for cocking; and then, while we waited, the rain would come.

We bolted up the other sections of the wheel next morning. It was a complete wheel again, and I should have been thrilled when, having removed the chocks with which we'd had to lock it while fixing the bolts, it turned with just the slightest push.

It was another exasperatingly fine morning, without even a cloud in the sky, but I was too hard-bitten to be taken in by that. The clouds would come, and so eventually would the rain, and although I was pleased to see the wheel turn, I felt no excitement.

271

Clow had to swank again.

"It looks a treat. I told you that I could fix it. Smooth as a top! If we had the sluice fixed and the bucket slats in, we could let the water on now and see it really going. But we'll have to leave it, I suppose."

The rain didn't come at its usual time and manner that day. It started before we had finished the tedding—a heavy shower that lasted only about ten minutes before the sun came out again, and it remained fine for the rest of the afternoon. It was no good. The shower had been too heavy, and although the sun was hot, there was no wind.

It was a test for anyone's nerves. It was all wrong, anyway, I thought, that farmers should be at the mercy of the weather like this, particularly in war time, when the production of food was so urgent. Haymaking, the way we were doing it, was a fantastic anachronism; I had read in a farmer's journal how it should be done. The crop should be cut when ripe and raked and conveyed straight away into a drying kiln. There, all moisture could be removed from it, leaving only its vital chemical constituents. It would be baled as it left the kiln, and there would be no need for stacking. This dried grass was in every way better than hay.

But a kiln cost thousands of pounds. It required either coal or oil fuel. Only a big farmer with hundreds of acres of grass could afford to invest in such an apparatus, whose utility was only seasonal. It seemed to me as that week dragged on that the only way to acquire peace of mind was to bow to the inevitable and regard the hay as lost. Rotted down, it would have a certain value to the land as fertiliser.

We fixed the sluice. I didn't need Clow's advice, or even his help in this, but he gave both. The slats for the buckets proved to be difficult, however. The slots for them were three quarters of an inch thick, and all my planks were an inch thick, which meant that their edges had to be reduced at each end—a tedious operation, made more so by my gloomy state of mind. I'd only got about half of them fitted when, on the tenth day from the actual mowing of the meadow, we knocked off for dinner.

The weather seemed to be following its usual pattern. It had been a fine morning. It would be a fine afternoon. We'd ted the hay, go along to Hendre, come back, and then the rain would begin.

But it didn't happen like this. There was the same northerly wind. There were clouds in the sky, but they didn't darken. Instead, towards the end of the afternoon, they began to clear, and the wind veered to east and strengthened. It was about six o'clock when we returned from Hendre to our own field.

Clow picked up a forkful of the hay, shook it out.

"It's right," he said. "We'll get it cocked. If it doesn't rain we'll have it led tomorrow. You go and let your good lady know about the baking, only we'll need all the help we can get now, with the cocking."

I bore these exciting tidings to the house. The baking must wait. Dain, Parkey and the elder children joined us in the field. Porgy would join us when she got the little children to bed. Clow had already started raking the hay into windrows, and the rest of us started on the cocking, big cocks this time.

We had no outside help. Every farmer in the district must have been too busy with his own crops in this providential change in the weather. The children had had their evening meal. We were not going to stop for ours, but when Porgy joined us, she brought out a can of tea and some sandwiches.

I was too excited to eat. Could it be possible that we were going to get the hay in, after all? Could it go the whole night and not rain? There was not a cloud in the sky. The sun was reddening as it sank lower, but there was no mist and the wind was dropping—it was still east, and it was dry as a desert wind. The children, in spite of their protests, were packed off at half past nine, Dain going with them to see them to bed. She returned with another can of tea.

We worked on, Clow helping with the cocking now, and by half past ten, just as the sun had set, the last cock was made. The job was done.

I didn't go to bed that night.

I sat in the John Nash room, with the shutters open. I dozed, but only as a dog dozes. I woke at intervals and went to the front door. The sky was clear, the stars glittering, as on a frosty night. The wind, still east, was blowing gently across the meadow, and the hay smell in it was as strong and as good as it had been on the first day after mowing.

I saw the sun rise. It was then only half past two by the clock, and Clow, when we had packed up, had said that ten was the earliest to start leading. Still eight hours to go! I went out and walked up and down between the rows of cocks, stopping here and there to feel them with my hands. There was not even a suspicion of dew on them. How awful, I thought, if between now and ten o'clock, the weather broke again. The sky was cloudless, the sun already warm, but it had happened before, just like this. It might happen again. Never had a space of time seemed so long ahead.

Fortunately I fell into a real sleep when I went back to my chair. I was roused by the usual noises of our wakening household from a nightmare. I had dreamt that we had been struck by a terrible storm, like a tropical cyclone. There had been thunder and lightning, a violent wind, a deluge of rain. The stream was a raging torrent. The dam wall had given way, and a huge tidal wave of water had swept over the meadow. The hay had gone. And in the middle of the stream an immense waterwheel spun like a Catherine wheel, with flames and sparks cascading from it.

Looking through the window, I was relieved to see that the hay was still there. The sun was shining, the sky was blue. It was a perfect day.

Clow arrived at half past nine. He had brought with him on the trailer a load of old wheat straw, which we spread for the foundation of the stack in the yard, between the cowhouse and the still unrepaired stable. He was in a good mood.

"We've got it at last," he said. "We couldn't have a better day. It will all be in by teatime, and not much the worse for its wetting either."

Tom, in his car, with Sara and Mrs Prophet and two other village women arrived punctually at ten, and Amy came soon after on her bicycle. Tom, by arrangement, had brought a case of beer, which he had wrapped up in a sack, and he said to me confidentially when we offloaded it:

"I covered it up like this so that old Elijah wouldn't see it, or he might have been tempted to come along. I hope you don't mind, but I told him there'd be nothing but tea and lemonade going today. That settled *him!*"

It seemed that no cart or wagon was going to be available. We'd do all the leading with the trailer, but as we'd decided to let the children skip school, they had harnessed Annabella to the trap and they were to do some leading on their own. There were no forks for them. They'd load with their hands.

I felt completely happy again. Certainly the most efficient method of winning hay was the modern one of cutting it and drying it in the kiln, and pressing it (all mechanically) into bales. But there could be no excitement doing it that way, no fun, nothing to make the workers sing as they started to do (there was no constraint today) as we began on the first cocks. And this was at least half our own hay, not such a good crop as the Jew's Harp's or Clow's had been, not in such good condition, but good enough.

We were going to get it in. We were not going to lose the money and the labour we'd spent on It. Farming was a good life after all.

Dain and Porgy had been up till late last night doing another baking. They had made another brew of beer the day before. We hadn't been able to get a joint, but they'd made a huge meat pie. They were not going to be shamed

276

by the spread that the Jew's Harp had put on.

At eleven, when we knocked off for our first refreshments, I went into the house to find that Albert had been, and in my mail was a packet from my photographer friend. It contained two films. I loaded the camera, and got my first snap of our helpers and the children gathered round the tractor, and Annabella and the loaded trap in it too. In spite of what he had said about breaking the camera, Clow had climbed on to the tractor seat and posed. It would be number one of the album of pictures we would send to his sister.

We carried on. The children who were not helping with the trap rode on the trailer for each trip from stack to field. There were clouds, but they were summery ones, floating high with even contours. The wind was east, dry and bland. And the stack was growing. Nearly half the field was bare when we stopped for dinner.

Two more men and a woman, they were strangers to me, joined us when we started again. They were from more distant farms, helping "we" because, I guessed, we would be helping "they"—and I imagined that Clow was not too pleased to see them. There was no sign of Thomas Hendre, but he would be busy with his own hay, and anyhow we had all the helpers we needed.

Round about three o'clock we gathered the last load, and we all followed it triumphantly to the stack. It wasn't as big as the first Jew's Harp stack had been. But to me it looked enormous. It was a good shape too, its sides and ends leaning outwards slightly as they rose, then slanting inwards like the roof of a house. Clow himself had ordered the building of it, with Tom and Amy helping.

He and Tom climbed up by a ladder on to it now, and they stood, one at each end as we pitched up the last of the crop. Tom came down when it was nearly done, leaving Clow to put the finishing touches on the ridge.

I had my camera handy and (not unwillingly) he posed again before he moved to the ladder to come down.

There was still some beer left. I ran and fetched it. Then, as we drank it, Amy struck up *Land of Our Fathers* again. I sang the words in English as well as I knew them. Victory! I squeezed Dain's hand. Everything had come right after all. No more worries. At last I could think with pleasurable anticipation about the waterwheel. I could look at the lake and really enjoy it.

Perhaps it was as well that Clow should remind me that there were other things besides our own hay, and the waterwheel and our lake.

"*Jowl*," he said, "and now we'll have to go and help Hendre, and there'll be someone else's tomorrow, and the next day too. There's no end to it. But never mind. We've got ours all right at last!"

21

IT WAS another spell of settled weather. We helped to get the Hendre crops in, and I was haymaking with Clow at other farms every day for more than another week. There was mowing to do as well as leading. There was no time to get on with the wheel. There was no time even to look at our oats and potatoes and roots, and I had to leave the gardening to Dain and Porgy and the children. The rains, and now the fine weather again, had produced a vigorous crop of weeds in the garden at least.

I was very happy to help these farmers, who were really only smallholders. They were all short-handed. Their farms were small and ill-equipped. This was primarily grazing country. Before the war, it seemed, they'd made a bare living with a few dairy cows, and rearing pigs and poultry, using bought food to supplement their hay for winter feeding.

The shortage and strict rationing of manufactured imported cattle foods had made things very difficult for them. They had been ordered to plough up a proportion of their grazing fields and grow crops. Without horses or implements, they had been forced into having it done for them by the committee or private contractors, and it was vital that what hay remained for them should be successfully harvested, and at no extra cost than that implied in the "we helps they and they helps we" principle.

They were in the opposite direction from Castle Druid to Castlebridge, and the Jew's Harp folk had nearer commitments. Most of the workers I met were strangers to me, and although they were friendly enough and there was plenty to eat and drink, there was not quite the same happy atmosphere of the Jew's Harp haymaking, or our own. The women were all elderly. They needed Amy to liven them and start them singing. Or perhaps it was just Clow whose very presence exuded a damping influence on their spirits. I had the feeling that he regarded them all with disdain, that helping them at all was a condescension on his part.

At one of the farms, called Langolem, was an old blacksmith's shop, now used as a junk store. Junk, of any description, had always held an irresistible fascination for me. It was near to the stackyard, and while we were having one of our breaks for refreshment, I had a look inside.

It must have been a long time since it was used for its original purpose. There was no anvil. The leather of the bellows had great holes in it. The first thing that struck my eye among the junk was the remains of a very ancient motor bike, that must have been involved in a crash, for the front wheel and handlebars were crumpled. It had been partly stripped. There was no tank, no saddle, no magneto. It was a vintage machine, belonging to the days before kick starters and clutches, when to ride you had to grasp the handlebars and push, first at a walk and then at a run until the engine fired, when you leapt into the saddle.

The power was transmitted from the engine to the back wheel by a V-section belt engaging a V-pulley welded to the spokes. I saw that the belt, although detached, was there, before my interest was diverted by something else half-hidden between a harrow and a defunct oil cooking stove. It was a cast iron cog wheel attached to a shaft, and when I moved the harrow and stove out of the way, I saw that the shaft was the same thickness as that of the waterwheel shaft. The cog wheel could be fixed on to our shaft.

I was feeling almost as excited as I had done when we had first looked at the waterwheel. If I could find a small cog wheel with teeth of the same pitch as the big one, to fit on a second shaft, then my gearing for the dynamo would be almost complete, needing only a pulley wheel to take the driving wheel or belt.

My luck was in. On a ledge just above the broken bellows, with a pile of old horse shoes, was not one but several cog wheels of different sizes, but with their teeth all of the same pitch as that of the big one. I tried a six-inch one, and it meshed perfectly. Then my eyes fell on the old motor bike again—on its back wheel with the V-pulley and the belt. If that wheel could be fitted on to the same shaft as the six-inch cog wheel, then my gearing was complete.

The wheel itself, so that the buckets would fill, should revolve slowly, say at ten revolutions a minute. Its cog wheel (or spur) was about seven feet in diameter. That on the shaft in which it meshed was nine inches so that the smaller one would rotate about nine times as fast—ninety revolutions a minute. It was the same principle as the crank wheel and hub of a push bike. The big cog wheel I had found was three feet. Meshed with the six-inch one it would multiply the speed on the second shaft by six, so that the bike wheel would have a speed of 540. Its pulley had a diameter of eighteen inches. If that of the dynamo was six, then the ultimate speed would be at least 1,600 revs, and that should be enough.

I said nothing to Clow about my find. But during the afternoon I took a chance, when he was out of hearing, of asking the farmer about the bike and the wheels. He was one of the two men who had helped with our own hay. The bike, he told me, had belonged to his brother, who'd been a blacksmith, but chucked it soon after the First War and emigrated to South Africa. A youth had tried to ride it one day and had smashed it up. It was only scrap, like everything else in the shop, but he'd been expecting someone from the Government to come and collect it as salvage. I offered him ten shillings for the bike and the wheels. He refused to take anything for them. They were no use to him. He'd be glad to get them out of the way.

Clow looked puzzled, and a little huffed, when, with the haymaking finished, I showed him my treasures and asked him to help me load them on to the trailer, but I offered no explanation.

"I suppose," he said, "the cog wheels are for the electricity. *Jowl*, if I'd known you were looking for things like that, I could have told you this man would have had them. His brother knew all about machinery and the like. But what do you want the old motor bike for?"

"Wait and see," I answered. "I want to try an experiment. It may work, and it may not. I'll show you when I get it fixed up."

No, I wasn't going to tell him yet. If I did, I knew by experience that he'd criticise and start making suggestions, and end up by claiming full credit for the idea if it worked successfully, as he had done for the dam wall and the installation of the wheel.

Certainly, I'd take a photograph of it when it was all fixed up, with Clow himself in the picture, to send Rosie. It wouldn't worry me then (especially in the light of what she had said in the postscript to her letter) what he told her, what credit he claimed. But I wanted the satisfaction of doing this part of the job entirely on my own. After all, I wasn't a fool. I had invented and made a collapsible lobster pot that worked!

We finished the last of our haymaking jobs on a Saturday, and although the war news was bad, with reports of heavy night raids on un-named British cities, and Rommel advancing towards Egypt, defeats and withdrawals in Russia and the Far East, I felt that I was justified in regarding Sunday as a part holiday, and getting on with the wheel. I knew of course that there were plenty of jobs waiting for me on the fields. There was weeding to be done. The swedes and mangolds should be thinned, and although the oats were too high now for weeding, I should at least have taken a walk round. But they looked all right from the house.

There was gardening to be done in the morning.

Three more "eight-and-six" toddlers, all girls from the East End of London, had been sent to us during the week, and Dain and Porgy had had their hands full. They and the other children might have had their heads full too if Dain hadn't noticed in time that the hair of two of the newcomers was heavily infested with lice.

Weeding was not the only job to be done in a garden, of course. There were slugs and caterpillars, and other pests to be found and dealt with. Seed beds had to be thinned, new planting to be done, which meant watering. We'd found a market for some of our produce in the travelling grocer who called once a week, but the prices he gave us were very low: twopence each, for example, for fat cos lettuces, for which in a shop the price would have been at least sixpence. The real profit in the garden was in what we were saving by not having to buy our vegetables at shops.

The elder children, especially Amelia and Makubwa, were a real help, and so were the others when it came to picking peas and fruit, provided there was someone to watch them and see that a reasonable proportion of what they picked went into their baskets or cans and not directly into their mouths. I would not trust even Amelia with the strawberries.

Theirs was all voluntary work, however, and I wouldn't have asked any of them for help on a morning like this, with so many more delightful things to do. It was really hot again, a heat wave. The water in the stream and lake was warm. I'd had a swim myself and I knew. I'd felt most reluctant to come out. They were nearly all there now, in the boat, swimming or paddling.

And only my conscience, my sense of duty, kept me at work. I was itching to get on with the wheel, to finish the boards for the buckets—the jobs I'd found so tedious when I'd been worried about the hay.

I should have them all done and fitted in a couple of hours. Then, for the first time, we could open the sluice and see the thing go. It wouldn't be the real test. I'd have to wait until I'd got all my machinery fixed up for that—more work that must be deferred for a time when there was nothing of greater urgency to do. Yet just to see the wheel turning would be an exciting prelude, one to record with another photograph. Clow would be coming in the afternoon, of course. I'd watch out, however, that it was not he who actually opened the sluice. That privilege should be for the children, if they could manage it.

I started on the boards immediately after dinner. The planks were drier than on the last day I had worked on them before leaving off to ted the hay. They were easier to saw and reduce to the right size, and I was working with a lighter heart. The hay was in. I'd done a really hard morning's stint at the garden, after more than a week's hard labour at our neighbours' hay fields. I had a clear conscience even about the mangolds and the potatoes. I would make up for leaving them this afternoon, by working until dusk every day next week.

And, after all, if my machinery and the dynamo worked all right, it would be at least a negative contribution to the war effort. It would be saving many gallons of imported paraffin.

Clow arrived about three o'clock. He was looking

very clean and spruce in a suit of jeans, which I guessed had been sent to him by his sister. By then I had sawn and rimmed all the boards, and I had only to hammer them into the oblique slots in the rim of the wheel. I didn't mind him helping with this job. He, too, seemed to be in a holiday mood. But that didn't stop him taking one of the boards from my hand and hammering it in himself.

He had walked over. There had been no reason for him coming to the house with the tractor since our haymaking, and he had offloaded the cog wheels and the motor bike at his own place. When he had fixed the board, he remarked:

"I've been having a look at those wheels we got the other day from Langolem. They'll be just the thing for gearing up the waterwheel to the dynamo. It puzzled me at first why you wanted the old motor bike. It came to me in a flash when I looked at the back wheel and the belt. You'll need another shaft for it, you know, to take that and the small cog wheel, with bearings at each end. It's all got to run smoothly. It's a pity we haven't got them all here now that we've got the wheel just about finished, so that we could work out just where everything has got to be fixed. Pass me another board."

I was vexed. Would he never let me do anything by myself? I wished that I hadn't told him about the wheels and the bike, that I had left them at the farm and then gone for them with Annabella and the trap, and kept it dark from him until the whole apparatus was ready to be fixed. Yet, I couldn't help admiring him for his detective work, and I had to laugh to myself at the way in which he was once again assuming a position of authority.

He hammered in the last board. Then he gave the wheel a powerful push, and it began to revolve, making two complete turns before its momentum was spent.

He stood back, surveying it admiringly.

"*Jowl*, it's a nice job. Couldn't be better. It's a pity we haven't got the rest of it connected up. What about the wiring? You'll need some heavy stuff for a lead up to the house. Will there be enough in what Eddy gave you? I'll give you a hand with all that when you're ready. I learnt how to do wiring when I was out on a building job in South Africa. No one could teach me anything about that. The only thing I never learnt was plumbing."

"I think I can manage the wiring all right," I said. "And that's a long way ahead. We shan't really need the lighting until the autumn."

"Righto. Well, what about letting the water on now? You won't have to give it full sluice to start it turning. Have you got your camera handy? Rosie's got to see a picture of this."

I said firmly:

"I don't want to start it until everyone's here. Stand by, and I'll let everyone know, and I'll go and get the camera."

It wasn't, I felt, such an occasion as the closing of the dam, but I'd have liked Eddy to be present and our friends at the Jew's Harp. There was no way now of letting them know.

Dain and most of the children were already at the lake. I shouted to her that we were going to start the wheel. By the time that I had returned with the camera they were crowding round the dam wall and the wheel and Clow, as I had anticipated, was standing at the sluice gate, ready to open it.

I felt reluctant to exercise my authority, and tell him not to. The situation called for tact. Suddenly, I was inspired. It is a characteristic of the boaster, the exhibitionist, that he should regard himself as possessed of just the opposite virtues—modesty, self-effacement. The man who belittles his own achievements, when they are real achievements, is often only indulging in another form of swank.

I said to Clow:

"You ought to have the honour of opening the sluice. I think we're all ready now. And I'll take a photo of you doing it."

My subtlety worked.

"No," he said, and his modesty was magnificent, "*You've* got to do it. It's your wheel. I've only rigged it up for you. It ought to be you or your good lady."

Dain declined, and I called to Angus and Makubwa, who were standing near.

"Come on. One on each side. Lift it up very slowly."

I had made the shutter of three independent oak boards, fitted into iron grooves on each side of the sluice, so that they could be raised or lowered. The top board rose about an inch above water level. Angus and Makubwa tugged at it, and suddenly the water gushed out between the bottom edge of it and the second plank, into the sluice itself.

I had watched this through the view finder of the camera, and I believed that Clow was in the picture when I snapped it. We all moved along the side of the sluice then, watching the water run along it, and we were just in time to see it reach the sluice end, pour into the topmost bucket and gush over into the next. And then the wheel began to move, at first slowly, and then with swiftly gathering speed until it was whizzing round almost like the Catherine wheel of my nightmare.

The children were screaming with delight. I squeezed Dain's hand. I congratulated Clow, and Clow, still with his well-assumed air of modesty, congratulated me. I knew as I watched the wheel that this was no proof of its ultimate efficiency. It was running free, doing no work. We hadn't even connected the original pinion shaft. It was spinning too fast for the buckets to fill. It was so well-balanced, and the axle bearings were so well greased, that a pint of water in one bucket just clear of the wheel top would have made it move, and momentum would have done the rest.

Yet, potentially, the power was there, and I couldn't help thinking what a curse it was that there was so much to be done on the farm, that we couldn't go and fetch the cog wheels and the motorbike now, and start rigging up the dynamo apparatus at once. In his present mood, I would not have minded Clow helping and giving me advice.

We let the wheel go on turning for a while. I took some more snaps, finishing the roll, Clow willingly posing again. Then we put the shutter back, and the wheel at last stopped. It was teatime.

That same evening, when all the children were in bed, I suggested to Dain that we should have a stroll round the fields. It was bothering me a little that I hadn't really seen them for so long.

The shortest and most agreeable route to the fields was by the lake and dam wall, and a path that branched upwards from that to the quarry. It was natural that we should pause by the wall, have another look at the wheel and gloat over it.

"Isn't it marvellous," Dain said, "that we've really got the waterwheel at last. Only I do hope that we'll be able to grind oats with it as well as make electricity. How exciting to have porridge, and make oat cakes, from oats we've grown ourselves!"

It was not beyond the bounds of possibility, I thought. The belt that drove the dynamo might just as easily work a hammer mill, but that again was still a long way ahead. And we had to harvest and thresh our oats before making oatmeal. I couldn't resist opening the sluice and letting the wheel run again. We watched it for a while. Then I turned it off, and we stood looking at the lake.

The trout were rising all over its surface. There were no really big ones yet, but those we did see were fat, and there could be no doubt that they were growing. By next year there should be at least half-pound fish.

The dinghy was moored near the shallow end. Dain said:

"Do let's have a pull in the boat, before we go up to the fields. We never seem to get a chance while the children are about. It would be just like old times, wouldn't it? The lake does remind me of our creek!"

Again I had a twinge of nostalgia, yet it was not a painful one. I was too much in the present. And the present seemed good. I had almost forgotten about the object of our walk.

We got into the dinghy, and we pulled around the lake, putting an end temporarily to the trouts' insect supper.

It was a beautiful evening, with the sun still well above the horizon. Dain was at the oars. Half closing my eyes, it was easy to imagine that we were pulling down our creek, out towards the sea, for a go at the mackerel. Yet it was just as pleasant to think about the waterwheel, and the hay, safely stacked, and no more anxiety about the weather.

But the midges were starting to bite, and shortly we pulled into the shore, moored the dinghy, and really set off on our walk. We came to the potato and roots field first. I was relieved when I saw the potatoes. There were plenty of thistles, and here and there bracken was growing up between the rows, but the haulms were well-advanced and healthy looking, and here and there they were already in flower.

The roots didn't look so good. It was hard to distinguish the swede and mangold plants from the weeds, until one looked closely. It was going to be a terrific job hoeing them and thinning them. But the last thing Clow had said, when we'd parted at teatime, was that we'd be starting on the roots in the morning, and we'd get the job done. It would be two months yet before the oats were ready for harvesting.

And the oats, as we approached the first field certainly were looking good. The plants were over two-and-a-half feet high, and I'd seen heads on them the last time I had been round. And now (we were still about fifty yards away) there were signs of ripening. Here and there were patches, not of green, but the colour of straw.

This surprised, but did not at first alarm me. It wasn't until we reached the field and I looked more closely at the nearest light-coloured patch that I got my first fright. The leaves, and the heads too, had changed to straw colour, not because they were ripe, but because they were *dead*. The grains were no bigger than pin heads. And then, examining the stem of one of the plants, I saw that it was stained with a fine powder, the colour of iron rust.

I looked at the adjoining, and still green, plants. They were alive, but their stems had the same stain upon them, and in tiny patches it was on their leaves.

I didn't want to alarm Dain. I was as certain as I could be that the stain was rust disease. It attacked certain garden plants, such as broad and runner beans. If the plants were sprayed with a fungicide at an early stage, it could be arrested, but if it got hold, the only treatment was to remove the plants, roots too, and burn them.

"I'm a bit worried about this," I said, trying not to sound worried. "It looks like rust disease. Let's go and look at the other fields. They may be all right."

There were two other fields adjoining. Both had the same deceptive light-coloured patches among the apparently healthy green. We walked in silence round the headlands, stopping now and again to examine the plants closely. We did not find one without that ominous-looking reddish brown stain, on its stem or on its lower leaves, and many of them were dead, the leaves and heads withered.

"Is it really bad?" Dam asked, when we got to the end of our tour. "Does it mean that we're going to lose the whole crop?"

"I don't know. We'll have to phone the Cultivation Officer in the morning and get him to come out and see it. He warned us, I remember, when I tried to sound him about getting a loan from the committee, that we might never harvest our oats—only I believe he was thinking about the weather. A good job we didn't get a loan."

"What about Clow? It will be his loss too. Oughtn't we to get him to come and have a look at it now?"

I remembered that Clow had told me that he was going to walk out to some distant farm this evening, to have a look at some young cows that were for sale. He might not have got home yet. And anyway, I didn't feel up to meeting him at present. He would only irritate me.

I was very worried indeed. If I was right in my diagnosis, the whole crop would have to be destroyed. Not only that, the fields would have to be ploughed up again, and treated with a soil fungicide, before any other crops could be sown. But what crop could be sown at this time of the year to produce any sort of fodder for the winter? The seed, probably most of the fertiliser, the labour that had gone into the production of the oats, would be a dead loss. Clow had said that we would have to buy two more cows for the winter, for both of the ones we had got would be dry soon. Our hay and the roots wouldn't keep them. There'd be more money needed for food, and so very little in the way of income to be set against it.

Why, I thought bitterly, had I ever let myself in for farming? What a simpler, and less nerve-racking, and more profitable business writing was! And yet, how often, when I had been trying to solve some baffling problem in the writing of a book, sitting cramped at my typewriter, drinking black coffee, smoking fag after fag, I had thought exactly the other way round.

Dain must have guessed how gloomy were my thoughts, for she put her hand on my shoulder and said:

"Cheer up, darling! Perhaps it is not as bad as it seems. The Government man may be able to tell us some way of treating the crop to kill the thing that's growing on it, and save it all. And anyway the potatoes are looking good, and so will the swedes and mangolds when we get them thinned out. And there's the waterwheel. That's a huge success. And never mind if we do have to buy our porridge for this year. We'll have some to grind next year, and perhaps some wheat too. And isn't it a lovely place we've got. Let's go and have another pull in the boat before it gets dark."

I had to laugh.

"And pretend we're going mackerel fishing!"

22

MY DIAGNOSIS was correct. Which of the various types of rust fungus it was that had attacked the plants, the officer could not say. It would require microscopic examination. There was no doubt it was a virulent type, although he had an idea that the withering of some of the plants might be due to some other disease, to which crops on newly ploughed land were very liable.

He knew of no chemical spray that would arrest the infection at this stage. Had there been one, it would have been mechanically impossible to apply, with the growth of the plants so advanced, unless it had been done with an aeroplane.

There was only one thing to do. The crop would have to be mown at once. It should be treated as we would treat hay, get it thoroughly dry and then burn it on the ground, and make certain that every bit of it was burnt. A strong fumigant should then be harrowed into the soil.

That should help to destroy the spores of the fungus, but it would be too risky to sow another cereal crop for two years at least. The safest thing would be grass, and in a case like this the official compulsion to grow cereals would be waived. It would be expensive, but in the long run it would pay. It would give us hay as well as first-rate summer grazing.

Clow said little when I first told him about the rust. We had walked round the fields together.

"I've seen this on oats before, but never quite so thick," he said. "I think maybe you're right in getting the Government experts out to see it, but I don't think much of them. We'll take anything they say with a grain of salt."

He had maintained a stony silence in the presence of the officer, leaving me to do the talking. He didn't deign even to thank or wish good day to the officer when he left us. But as soon as he was out of hearing he remarked sarcastically:

"*Jowl!* You'd wonder where they get all their knowledge from!" And then, surprisingly, he added: "But I'll not say he isn't right about turning all this into grass, only it's a pity he didn't say so before, and not let us waste our money and labour growing oats."

"But he did," I protested. "It was the first thing he did say when he came round before. But it was a Government order that cereals should be sown."

"Then the bloody Government should know better. Anyway, that can't be helped now. What I did say is that grass might be a better crop than oats. If we'd sown grass in the spring, we could have been grazing these fields with cows and bullocks in the backend up till Christmas, and maybe longer, with a soft winter. We'd have a good crop of hay next summer and grazing again after that. You know, if ever you wanted to sell Castle Druid to another gentleman, you'd likely get more for it if it was all good grass, and not part arable. It isn't everyone who wants to be troubled with ploughing and sowing."

He was puzzling me. He seemed to be regarding our catastrophe very lightly.

"But I don't want to sell it."

He gave me one of his shrewd looks.

"No. Of course not." He paused, and then: "What I'm trying to tell you is that apart from what we've lost on the oats, it may be a good thing in the long run, for making the farm pay. I saw two nice cows, where I went last night. Shorthorns. One of them's newly calved, second calf. The other's due in September. We ought to have them both. The man asked a hundred and twenty pounds for the pair of them, and it would be a hundred and fifty if we got them in the market."

He was frightening me.

"But we can't afford them, Clow, if we're losing our oats, and now having to re-sow the fields with grass. And what are we going to feed them on in the winter?"

I didn't know exactly what the state of the joint account was at present. I was leaving everything to Porgy. But I knew, and Clow knew, there was precious little left of our joint capital of £500. Apart from the cows we had bought, we'd had to buy most of their fodder. There had been the seed for the crops, the fertilisers, fuel for the tractor. Against this on the credit side was only the sale of the milk, and that barely exceeding the cost of the fodder. And my own bank account was running dangerously low.

"Must we buy both cows?" I asked. "Couldn't we do with one?"

Again Clow looked at me shrewdly.

"We've got to have them both," he answered. "As a

matter of fact, I've bought them. It was a chance too good to be missed. But if you're hard up, then there's no need for you to put anything down on them. Let it stand over. Call it a loan if you like."

A loan? Was this just generosity on Clow's part—the "heart of gold" of his sister's postscript? How much money had she sent him? Obviously more than he had spent on the tractor, unless he had considerable savings of his own. If I got into his debt, it would alter the balance of our partnership. He was already bossing me.

I looked him straight in the face. He met my gaze unflinchingly. I was convinced of his sincerity and goodwill, yet I was still frightened.

"It's very good of you, Clow," I said. "I am hard up, of course. We're losing money with the evacuee children. But I'd rather pay my way, and I'll go halves with the cows. But it's a blow about the oats, and having to buy extra food until next spring."

Was he disappointed with my answer? I had the feeling that he was. But he laughed and said:

"We'll manage somehow." And then: "Well, we'd better get on with the job. It's murder—mowing and burning crops that have got on as well as these. We'd have had a nice stack from them for the winter. But it can't be helped. We'll have to leave the roots until it's done. I'll go and bring the tractor and the mowing-machine. Have you taken a photo of the oat fields, by the way? "

"No. I hadn't thought of it. But I've got another film. I'm sending the other one to be developed and printed."

"Well, it would be nice to have one, before we start

on the mowing. I don't suppose it would show the disease on them. You've got to look close to see it anyway. And by the way, if you or your good lady are writing to Rosie about the things she sent, you'd best not say anything about having to burn the crops. Don't mention it. I'll just send her a photo."

It was haymaking again, but haymaking without any thrills. And, ironically, we had perfect haymaking weather for our grim job of destruction. It took us two days to mow the three fields. The sun was so hot, the air so dry, that the swaths (in spite of the brown stain) began turning straw colour on top in a matter of hours, giving us the tantalising illusion of ripeness. It seemed wicked that all of it had to be burnt, for it looked, unless you looked closely, like a wonderful crop.

We'd have to give it at least two days to dry before tedding it. We started on the hoeing and thinning of the swedes and mangolds, a task which to me looked as though it might well last until the autumn, for the drills were closer together than the potato rows. Even in a garden, the job of thinning plants called for skill and concentration. If there were two or three close together, you had to decide which was the healthiest of them, and remove the others without disturbing the roots; and the spaces between the plants selected for survival should all be the same. And again, for each swede or mangold, there was at least one thistle to be cut or uprooted.

It was a monotonous, back-breaking job. I found that the only efficient way to do it was to kneel on a sack and use my bare hands, except for the really thick thistles. Clow did the mangolds, I did the swedes.

There was a satisfaction in looking back on a row and seeing in it nothing but the little green-plumed, yellow-purple bulbs, all nicely spaced and clear of weeds, free now to take nourishment from soil and sunshine, but the sight of the rest of the field waiting to be done discouraged any ecstasy. Indeed, I was feeling very gloomy and worried, and not only because of the oats.

I had gone into the partnership accounts with Porgy. Our working capital had now shrunk to less than a hundred pounds, and against that would have to be reckoned the cost of the new cows, and the re-sowing of the oat fields. Apart from the milk, the only thing our farming was going to produce for a year at least, was the potato crop.

It was clear that my own loss was heavier than I had bargained for. On the poultry and garden there had been practically nothing but expenditure. We had bought fifty laying pullets at a cost of a pound apiece. They had produced eggs, some of which we had sold, but as with the garden produce, a large proportion had gone for our own consumption. Every one of the children had a fresh egg three times a week.

We would make up on the poultry when our own reared chicks (we had over two hundred of them) started to lay in the winter, but until they did, they had to be fed, largely on bought food.

Our weekly grocery bill was terrific. The fees for the paying children did not make up for what the "eight-and-sixers" were costing in food and clothing. The school was running at a loss, and now, with the coming of the summer holidays, the loss was going to be heavier. The mother of the twins had recovered from her illness. She wanted to take them to Ireland for a holiday. Two more paying ones would be away for the holidays too.

And my own bank balance now stood at less than three hundred pounds.

I had discussed the general situation in private with Dain, when I had told her about the cows and Clow's offer to lend us our share of the price of them.

"I think," she said, "that it was very nice of him to offer to help like that, but I'm glad you didn't accept. Not that I don't trust him. I think he's absolutely straight, and we had to have the cows anyway. But we don't want to get into debt with anybody. It's bad enough that we still owe so much to the man who sold Castle Druid to us. I'll never really feel happy about Castle Druid until that is paid off, and it's really ours."

"But you're still glad we've got it, aren't you?"

She answered without hesitation:

"Of *course!* It's just right for us, isn't it? It's a marvellous place. We couldn't have found anything better, especially for the children. If only we had more money, so that we could have just the poor evacuees, and not bother about getting paying ones."

"There won't be any evacuees when the war's over," I said. "Do you want us to go back to Yorkshire then, to our old home?"

"You mean—and sell Castle Druid?"

"We couldn't afford both places. We can't now, really."

"I loved it there," Dain answered, "but I don't think I'd like to go back and see it all in a mess—the fields torn up for quarries, our lovely oak wood cut down. Besides, the war isn't over yet. It's no use worrying about what is going to happen when it is. We've just got to carry on here somehow or other. Don't you think we'd better sell Adder Howe?"

I had already realised that it was inevitable that we should do so, but I had funked saying so to Dain. It had been for us both at least the part fulfilment of a dream, a house built to our own design, in an almost ideal situation on our beloved Yorkshire coast. True that it was too far from the seashore for us to keep a boat. We had our compensation for this in the little trout stream that ran through our land, and in the sweep of unspoilt moorland that reached from our boundaries. Nor had I been able to realise my dream of a lake and having a waterwheel to make electricity.

There had been several other snags to Adder Howe, that had become more apparent as the size of our family had increased. We were six miles from the nearest township, and all our supplies had to come by road, easy enough in spring, summer and autumn, but difficult and sometimes impossible in winter, for we were six hundred feet above sea level, and the road often was blocked with snowdrifts. We didn't mind this, but we had found it impossible to get any permanent domestic help. Maids, nannies liked cinemas, dances, boyfriends for their time off, not nature study. And who could blame them?

Actually, since we had come to Wales, we had received an unsolicited offer for the purchase of Adder

302

Howe. It was from a house agent, acting on behalf of an un-named client, who had seen the place and would like to buy it and live in it as soon as it was de-requisitioned by the War Office, either before or at the end of the war. It was unfortunate, the agent said, that the value of the property had diminished, as it was likely that even after the war, the War Office would be using the adjoining moor as an artillery range and military training ground, and he strongly advised me to accept his client's offer.

It is naught, it is naught, saith the buyer! The offer was six hundred pounds. We had paid three hundred pounds for the land and spent more than twice that on the house. I had ignored the letter. After my talk with Dain I had written to the agent, telling him that although I thought his client's offer absurd, I might consider selling it at a reasonable figure. In my opinion, it was worth at least fifteen hundred pounds.

But even if we sold Adder Howe, and got fifteen hundred pounds for it, five hundred of it would have to go within another two years to pay off the Castle Druid mortgage. The balance would hardly see us through another two years, and by then we would be completely broke. If only I could get down to writing again! But how could I when I was working full out on the farm and garden and poultry? I had made many attempts to get on with my abandoned novel, but without any real success.

The weather could not have been more favourable for the incineration of the oats. Unlike the hay, not a drop of rain had fallen on it since it had been mown, and the dew had been very light. It was a fine sunny day, with a westerly wind, but we waited until the afternoon to make sure. I guessed that the children at least would enjoy the spectacle, and as they were now on holiday, all except the toddlers were there.

To them I made light of our reasons for burning the crop. It was diseased, and we would grow something in its place. Some of them helped by making torches of the twisted straw, and running along the windward side of the field. It went like a prairie fire, and I could have enjoyed the spectacle myself, if I hadn't been oppressed by the true significance of what we were doing.

Clow didn't seem a bit upset. As we stood watching the waves of hissing, crackling flame sweep across the field, he said to me:

"It's going well. That should kill the damned disease. There's nothing like burning for purifying. I'll start ploughing up tomorrow. We'll have it all sown again before the end of the month. By next spring all this will be beautiful grass, and we'll have a hay crop from it, better hay than the meadow."

Next spring! What would be happening by then? I wondered gloomily. We'd be lucky if Castle Druid was ours. We might indeed, be bankrupt.

I sat up late that night, making one more effort to get on with the book, re-reading what I had already written in the hope of picking up the threads of the story, of finding the momentum of creation which had eluded me for so long. It was no good. I had been working at the roots practically the whole day. My brain just wouldn't work. I had to give it up.

*　　　*　　　*

As Clow wouldn't let me drive the tractor, and nearly all the operations in the re-sowing of the fields were single-handed, there was nothing for me to do but get on with the roots. Dain or Porgy gave me a hand, usually in the afternoon or evening, and the children too volunteered to help, but I wouldn't accept their offer. It was their holiday, and it was right that they should enjoy themselves while the weather was so favourable for outdoor play and pastimes.

They were all happy enough. The war meant little to them. There was the lake, and the paddling Lido, the boat and the stream, the three ponies. Most of the city evacuees had been pale-faced, under-nourished—or, what was as bad, wrongly nourished—when they had arrived. Wholesome food, regular hours, fresh air and sunshine had worked wonders with them. They were all healthy, full of vitality, brown with the sun, and they were learning things too, apart from what they were learning in our own and the village school. They were living in the real country.

Several more parcels had arrived from the good-natured Rosie. Every child had some sort of garment of Canadian origin. She had also sent a miniature Indian wigwam and two feather head-dresses which the children took turns in wearing. Moulted feathers from the hen run were eagerly collected and made up in imitation of these adornments, and Amelia showed considerable originality and skill in painting tribal marks on some of the children with paint (luckily not oil paint) from our nursery school.

My newspaper friend had had the first of our spools

305

developed, with duplicate press enlargements of each of the sixteen snaps. The ones of the haymaking, particularly the one with Clow on top of the stack, were very good, and so was the one of Angus and Makubwa opening the waterwheel sluice, with Clow well in the picture.

I had taken views of the wheel itself, the lake, with the children in the boat, and swimming and paddling, of Makubwa and Angus fishing.

Clow was delighted with them. We gave him one set to send to his sister. He wanted to pay for them but I couldn't let him do this, for we were deeply indebted to Rosie for all the things she had sent us.

There was no holiday for me, of course. While Clow ploughed and harrowed and sowed and rolled the fields, I went on with the roots, day after day. I wouldn't have minded doing this, in fact I could have enjoyed it, if I hadn't been so worried about money, for the thinned-out and weeded rows were looking very good indeed.

I had transferred one hundred pounds from my private account to the partnership account, so that the cost of the new cows, and of the grass seed, could be met by us jointly. The balance in my own account would barely see us through to the end of the autumn.

I'd had a most depressing letter from the house agent in answer to my own. His client was still interested in the property, but it was going to be difficult to persuade him to make any substantial increase on his original offer. Whatever the property had been worth before the war, I must realise that it could not possibly fetch that value now. If I would state my lowest price, he would put that up to his client and give me his decision in due course. I had written to say that my lowest figure was one thousand pounds, and I had received no answer at all.

I hadn't touched the wheel since the evening of our walk, when we had made our tragic discovery about the oats. The children had pestered me about it: why wouldn't I make it go again? What was the good of it?

I had told them that although it was very nice to see it going round and round, it was no use making it do this until I had got all the machinery fixed, so that it would make our electricity. I was going to do it just as soon as I found time. My only progress towards this was that I had persuaded Clow to bring the cog wheels and shaft and the old motor bike, and dump them near to the wheel.

Yet I had thought plenty about the wheel. It would soon be autumn, the end of double, and then of single summer time. The days would be shortening. It would be a great convenience, and a considerable saving in our fuel bill, when we got the whole thing working, with lights at least in the downstairs rooms.

I was still determined that I was going to do it without Clow's advice or help. He was engaged with the rolling of the new-sown fields, a job in which he had again declined my help, when, one afternoon, I came to the end of the last row of roots. He was at the farthest field, out of sight, and, feeling rather like a boy playing truant from school, I hurried down by a route which kept me completely hidden from him. I went to the house for my tools, then back to the wheel.

I had got it all worked out in my mind. I would need a heavy rectangular timber frame to take the bearings of the two shafts, with a platform at the end of it on which the dynamo would be securely bolted. The frame would have to be rigidly bolted to the ground foundation, and be of sufficient height to give clearance for the big cog wheel, and the shafts would have to be in perfect alignment.

Physical work, provided it is work you like doing, is a perfect antidote to mental fatigue and worry. And this was a job I liked doing. I had a clear conscience, too. I'd finished the roots. The material I was using, apart from a few bolts and nails and a bucket of cement, was all scrap, which wouldn't have justified the expense of sending it to a foundry for resmelting. Apart from the waterwheel, there wasn't more than a hundredweight of iron and steel. And it was all going to be put to a most excellent use. And how much more pleasant a job it was than thinning and weeding roots. My worries about the war— about money, our unsold property, our future— temporarily, at least, lost their urgency.

It was not an easy job, however. I would have been glad of Clow's help for the sawing of the timber for the frame, and later for fixing the big cog wheel on to the first shaft, for I had to file a portion of the shaft flat in order to drive in an iron wedge for a locking key. Makubwa, Angus and Timothy were with me, all deeply interested in what I was doing, and eager to help. The only help they could give me was in holding things, or passing tools.

Yet I was managing without Clow, even in the very difficult operation of aligning the first shaft, so that the original small cog meshed snugly with the big spur of the waterwheel. I tested this by giving the waterwheel a heave and a couple of slow turns. The shaft rotated proportionately faster, and the new cog wheel I had fixed to it turned at such a rate that its teeth were blurred. The children were thrilled.

I could hear the sound of the tractor on the invisible fields and I thought that I wouldn't have minded if Clow had come down now to witness the success of the first stage of my apparatus. On reflection, I thought he was better where he was. It would be best to have the whole thing finished before he saw it.

I might have known that it wouldn't happen like that. Late in the afternoon I heard the tractor stop. Often Clow went straight home from the fields without calling at the mansion. But ten minutes later I heard his footsteps on the dam bridge, and he came down to the wheel. The children were still with me. I had just started unbolting the rear wheel of the motor bike from its frame.

I was not certain whether Clow was vexed or not. He was silent for a time, just looking at my handiwork. I said to him, innocently:

"I finished the roots, and I thought I might as well get on with this. I've got the first shaft fixed and it seems to work all right. Now I've got to get the other cog wheel and the bike wheel on the outer shaft."

"Yes, I can see what you've done. But you'll have to have your wood frame spiked down well into the ground. I'll give you a hand with it. I see you're doing it the way I told you. You'll need a heavy board across the frame to take the dynamo. *Jowl!* If you had the cables fixed, we could have had it working tonight. Let me have a look at that bike wheel. Now, if you like to go and get the dynamo and the cable, I can fix the second shaft for you. You could fix your wires to the trees for the time being. and have proper posts later."

It was no use. I couldn't refuse his help without risking a row with him. And anyway, it would be exciting to get the thing finished, and put it to the test. It wouldn't be necessary, I thought, to wait until I had got the wiring of the house completed. That would be a long job.

The cable from the dynamo would have to be connected to the charging board, which had an amp-meter, and a cut-out, and when the installation was complete, the current would go first to the batteries, and the supply would be drawn from them. The "cut-out" was an automatic device for preventing the battery charge leaking back to the dynamo. I hadn't decided yet where we should fix the charging board or the batteries. But all that we needed to prove that the whole contrivance worked was a lamp connected to the lead from the dynamo. If that lit up when we opened the sluice and the waterwheel began to rotate, all would be well. We could control the speed with the sluice itself, running the wheel very slowly at first, then increasing it gradually to its maximum. If the current proved excessive and the lamp burnt out, that wouldn't matter.

The children were holding things, passing tools to Clow now. I didn't mind. I hurried up to the house for the dynamo, some wire, a lamp and a lamp holder.

It was long past teatime when we had got the whole thing assembled, the cog wheel and the bike wheel fixed on the second shaft, the dynamo bolted on to the frame, with the belt joining its pulley with that of the bike wheel. It wouldn't have surprised me then if Clow had said:

"Well there you are! I told you I could fix it up for you!"

But he didn't. He stood looking at it for a while in silence, then he said:

"It's a clever job, that, a real clever job. You've done well to have thought it all out. It might have taken me months, and *jowl*, I don't think I'd have ever thought of using an old motorbike wheel and belt for it. Very clever. But will it work? Have you got the lamp properly connected up? Let's give it a trial."

I began to feel a little shaky. Here at last was the final act. We'd got our lake (with trout in it), we'd got our waterwheel, the machinery, the dynamo. But would it work?

This time I didn't want an audience. I half wished that Angus and Makubwa and Timothy were not with us, for they were going to be very disappointed if things went wrong. I took a final look at the cog wheels, felt the belt, made certain the connections to the lamp holder were secure. I had tied the lamp to the branch of a tree clear of the wheel. Then I said to Clow:

"Righto. You let the water in, very slowly, and I think you ought to stand by at the sluice ready to shut it. Something may break when we get the full force on it."

I told the children to stand back. Clow gently raised the top board of the sluice. Again I watched the water running along the sluice, and then pouring into the first bucket. The bucket filled. The wheel did not move. The water spilled over into the next bucket. Still it did not move. And then Clow shouted:

"Give it a push. That's all it needs. A push to start it."

I moved to do so, but before I touched the wheel it began to move: very slowly, and so did the other wheels, each one faster, with the bike wheel turning so that its spokes were invisible. The dynamo was spinning, purring.

I looked at the lamp. It was broad daylight with the sun shining. But at the base of the filament there was a distinguishable orange glow which quickly became brighter, and then a dazzling incandescence. The children gave excited shouts. I joined Clow at the sluice. Even the top board was only partly open. The waterwheel was moving at not more than a quarter of its possible working speed. There would be ample power to light the whole mansion and farm.

I felt triumphant, but I tried not to show it, lest Clow should think I was crowing over him. He was still in a generous mood, however.

"*Jowl*," he said: "it works a treat. A real treat. Especially that old motorbike wheel. I wouldn't have thought of that in a month of Sundays. It's clever. Now what about having another photograph? I'd like Rosie to see one of this."

23

IT WAS September. The holidays were over. Although the weather was now rather unsettled, the district corn harvest had begun. There was no corn harvest for us of course, but there was the same obligation on us to help our neighbours. We'd need their help when it came to the lifting of our potato crop.

The war situation continued to be grave, with little to justify the hope of an early victory over the three Axis powers. It seemed that Rommel's drive towards Egypt had been at least temporarily checked, yet there was no sign of any powerful Allied counter offensive. In Russia the Nazis were still advancing on the Caucasus. It seemed impossible that Stalingrad could last out much longer. In the Far East the Americans hadn't had time yet to organise a comeback against the victorious Japs. In the West there had been a gallant landing of troops, mostly Canadian, at Dieppe as a test of Nazi defences, which had proved tragically efficient. The Royal Air Force had increased the weight and frequency of its attacks on German war installations and factories, but the squadrons of Flying Fortresses, which later were to pattern bomb these targets by daylight, were still on the assembly line, on the other side of the Atlantic.

The Nazi raids on British cities continued. There had been a heavy raid on Bristol with heavy civilian casualties. We had been asked if we could accommodate four more toddler evacuees. If we had been asked to take a dozen of them we could not have refused, but I was more than worried about it. I didn't see how we could possibly carry on, certainly not more than a few more months.

I had heard at last from the house agent. His client had agreed to increase his offer to £750, but that was his absolute limit. We must take it or leave it. Very reluctantly we had decided to accept. We had received the customary deposit of ten per cent, with the balance to be paid on the completion of the conveyance. We had burnt our boats so far as Yorkshire was concerned. If we reckoned against this what we owed on Castle Druid, our total wealth in cash was under three hundred pounds. By the same token Castle Druid was completely ours. Yet for how long?

We'd had another double blow. The mother of the twins had decided to stay on in Ireland for the duration of the war. The two other paying evacuees who had left for the holidays were not returning. Our only payers now were Makubwa and Christine, and they were paying only thirty shillings a week.

It had been raining, putting a stop to all harvesting activities, the day the letter came asking if we could take the four new evacuees. We'd arranged to go to Hendre with the tractor and binder, but I had seen nothing of Clow all day. It cleared in the evening and I thought I had better walk over and see him to discuss our plans for the morning. I asked Dain to come with me, for it would give us a chance of a private talk.

Our nearest way to Clow's was over the dam bridge, and up over the top fields. Again we halted when we got to the bridge, with the lake on one side of us, the wheel below. I had by this time fixed a cable from the dynamo to the house, where in one of the small box rooms I had fixed the charging board and batteries. I had wired the kitchen and all the downstairs rooms. The light we got was not so bright, and not quite so steady as a town supply, but it was better than oil lamps, it was reliable, and it was costing us nothing. The wheel was now turning.

"Well that's a success, anyway," I said to Dain. "We wanted a waterwheel to make our own electricity, and there it is, we've got it, and we've got at least another three months to enjoy it, perhaps six months if we go carefully."

"Yes, and we've got the lake too," she answered quickly, "and the house and a home, and not just for ourselves either. And it's nice to think that now we've sold Adder Howe, we'll be able to pay off the mortgage, and all this will be ours."

"Darling," I said. "It won't be much use it being ours if we can't earn enough to run it on. Sooner or later, unless a miracle happens, we'll have to sell it, or borrow on it, which would amount to the same thing."

She was silent for a time. We were now both looking at the lake. It was deserted. The children were all in bed. The dinghy was moored to a tree branch. The air was a little chilly. There was no fly on the water. No rising trout. There were gleams of yellow in the bracken on its far bank, reflected on the lake's unruffled surface, and I knew before she spoke that Dain was thinking of our Cornish creek. But I was surprised when she said illogically:

" Wouldn't it be wonderful if the war was over, and we had just pots of money, and we could go back to Cornwall and build another house, close to our creek, or perhaps just have our old hut, and make it bigger, so that in summer at least we could have other children to stay with us, like Mary and the London kids who'll have to go back to live in smoky towns when the war is over. Wouldn't that be just wonderful?"

For one moment I allowed my mind to soar. Our old home, so far as we knew, was still there. We had heard from time to time, of various people who had lived in it, but only during the summer months. It was likely that if we ever wanted it, we could get it again, probably buy it. But one of our strongest reasons for leaving it was that it was too primitive for the rearing of our family. It would indeed need pots of money to make it into a decent home.

It was Dain who brought us both down to earth.

"It's silly to think of such things, isn't it? We've just got to carry on here somehow or other. It's such a perfect place for all the children. We've got to have the new evacuees. Don't you think if we wrote to the authorities telling them that we're hard up, they might help us? If we told them we may have to give it up surely they'll do something. And anyway we have got enough money to carry on through the winter. I wonder if we wrote to

Clow's sister, telling her everything, she would help? I did tell her in my last letter how difficult it was to get clothes and boots for the children and how grateful I was for what she had sent. And I told her too that the money we got for the evacuees didn't pay for what it cost to keep them."

I didn't answer, for I heard footsteps on the path on the other side of the dam. It was Clow. He walked on to the bridge, smiled and touched his hat to Dain.

"Good evening to you, ma'am."

"We were on our way to see you, Clow," I said. "Shall we be harvesting tomorrow?"

"No. Least not in the morning. There's been too much rain today. The lake looks pretty, doesn't it? I see the wheel's still working all right. Did you have a letter from Rosie this morning?"

" No," Dain answered.

"Well, she's written to you, and sent off some more parcels. I got a letter from her. She's pleased as Punch with the photos. She says she can't get over the improvements we've done to Castle Druid, especially the mansion itself. There's something else she says, but maybe we'd better wait until you get her letter. It had better come from her and not me. I've just been having a look at the fields by the way. The roots are looking well, and *jowl* there's a flush of grass starting to show in the first of the oat fields I've re-sown. It's the rain that's done it."

I tried to appear enthusiastic.

"That's wonderful," I said. "Shall we go and have a look at it?"

"Well you can if you like, but I wanted to go and have a look at the stable roof and the cottage. I was thinking that if there's no harvesting tomorrow, we might make a start putting them to rights. And I'd like to make a start on the front garden. I told Rosie that we were going to do that when we got a chance. I don't think it's going to be such a big job doing the stable, and you said you wanted it before the winter didn't you, ma'am?"

Dain gave me a worried glance.

"I don't think the stable is so important," she said. "We'd only need it for the ponies in the hardest weather."

I took my cue from that. It was no good trying to bluff. Clow had better know the bitter truth.

"I'm afraid we'll have to leave the stable and the cottages and the front garden." I said. "We just can't spend any more money on Castle Druid. The truth is we're practically broke. It looks as though we shan't be able to carry on here much longer. We're losing money on the farm. We've lost four of our paying evacuees. Now we've been asked to take four more non-paying ones. I think we'll have to sell Castle Druid before very long and clear out."

He was looking at me very earnestly.

"Sell it, and clear out, the whole lot of you? And have you got anywhere else to go?"

"As a matter of fact we haven't at present, for we've sold our Yorkshire home, at a very heavy loss. But we might be able to go back to where we lived in Cornwall. I don't know how it will affect our partnership if we sell up, Clow, but of course you'll get back what you've put into it. I'm very sorry to have to say all this, but it's best for you to know the truth."

"Of course it is," he answered slowly. "Of course it is. I've always said I like things straight. And I'm very sorry to hear things have gone bad with you. But you don't want to leave Castle Druid do you?"

"Certainly not until the war's over. We wanted to farm, and grow food, and have evacuees, and we couldn't do either in that Cornish place, even if we could get it. After the war there wouldn't be any evacuees, and probably we would have had to sell, for the mansion would be too big for us then, and I don t know that I'm really cut out for farming, much as I like it. I'm really a writer."

Again Clow was silent; and then he said, very deliberately:

"Now listen. You've been straight with me. I'll be straight with you. You haven't done anything about selling Castle Druid yet, have you?"

"No. Of course not."

"Right. Then listen. I'd have bought it years ago, if I'd had the money. As I've told you before it was mine and my sister Rosie's by rights. But I never had the money. Rosie would have bought it for me, but her husband always kept her close so far as money went. He was a stingy devil. Rosie always wanted to come back to Wales and live. I think her idea in coming here just before the war was to persuade her husband to buy the spot. And she'll buy it now if you want to sell, but she won't come here until the war's over. She'd be pleased enough for things, to go on as they are, but she'd like to go on having more improvements, and she wouldn't want to turn you

319

out.

"What she said in her letter that I didn't tell you, but I might as well tell you now, is that she'd like to send another ten shilling a week for each of the Government evacuees, so you won't lose money on them. And what I say now is that if you want to sell, she'll buy, and at a fair price, as much as you gave for it, and then for all you've spent on it, including all that you've paid me. We can work that out from my wage book. If you want the partnership to stand, all right. But if you don't, I'll run the farm and buy more stock, and you can help with the farm as much as you like and be paid for doing it, but not if you want to use your time for your other work. Rosie says that you ought to be writing, for she's read one of your books and says it's very good . . . Well, what do you think of it?"

I looked at Dain. Her eyes were brimming with tears. And then I looked at Clow, and I reached out my hand to him. I knew that we could trust him and I said to him, without any envy, and with complete sincerity:

"Clow, I think it's a wonderful proposition. I think Rosie must be an angel. I do want to get on with my writing, but I want to farm too, and we both want to go on with the evacuees until this damned war is over. But Castle Druid would be too big for us then, and, much as we like the place and you Welsh people, I think we'd be better by the sea, and we love Cornwall. I think the answer is yes—don't you, Dain?"

"Yes," Dain answered. "It sounds wonderful."

I laughed and I said, and I did not mean it ironically: "Gosh, Clow—you'll be the real Squire of Castle

Druid!"

"*Jowl*," he answered modestly. "I wouldn't say that. A rough chap like me. But Rosie's a lady all right. You wait till you see her. *Jowl*, that waterwheel goes well. I'm damned if I'd ever have been able to work it out as well as that. Come on now and let us have a look at the stable."

THE END

About the author

LEO WALMSLEY was born in Shipley, West Yorkshire, in 1892, and was brought up in Robin Hood's Bay on the North Yorkshire coast — the 'Bramblewick' of several of his novels. After serving with distinction in the Royal Flying Corps in the Great War, where he was awarded the Military Cross, he determined to become a writer, beginning with boys' adventure stories.

He lived for a while in London before returning to Robin Hood's Bay in the late 1920s, then settled in Fowey, Cornwall and wrote *Three Fevers* (1932), the first of his 'Bramblewick' novels, followed by *Phantom Lobster, Foreigners, and Sally Lunn.*

In addition to over twenty books, he wrote 200 or so short stories and articles prior to his death in 1966.

Other books available in this series

For further information about Leo Walmsley,
membership of the Walmsley Society,
or where you can buy these books,
please visit:

www.walmsleysoc.org

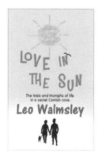
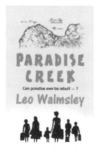
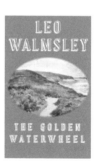

Published by
www.walmsleysoc.org